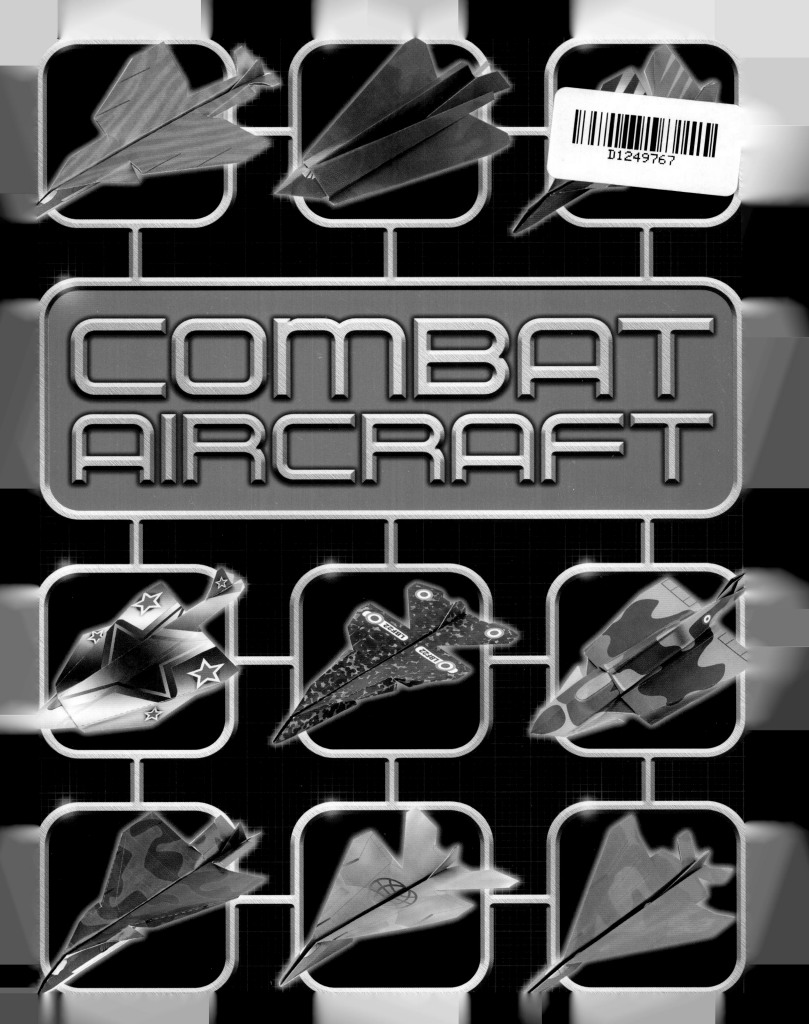

COMBAT AIRCRAFT

COMBAT AIRCRAFT

imagine
THAT!™

Imagine That! is an imprint of Top That! Publishing plc
27101 Breakers Cove, Valencia, CA 91355
www.topthatpublishing.com

FOLDING TIPS

■ *Before you start folding, make sure your paper is the correct shape.*

■ *Fold on a flat surface, like a table or a book.*

■ *Make your folds and cuts neat and accurate.*

■ *Crease your folds into place by running your thumbnail along them.*

■ *Carefully score along the marked lines using safety scissors and a ruler. This will make folding easier, especially as the lines become obscured toward the end of the model-making.*

SYMBOLS AND BASIC FOLDING PROCEDURES

These symbols show the direction in which paper should be folded. Although you'll not use them all in this section, you can use them to make up your own planes.

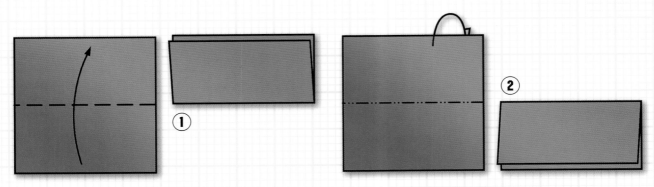

1. VALLEY FOLD (FOLD IN FRONT)   **2. MOUNTAIN FOLD (FOLD BEHIND)**

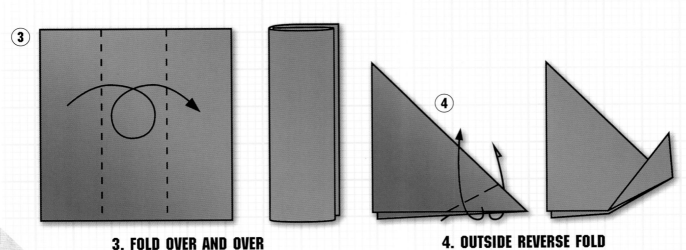

3. FOLD OVER AND OVER   **4. OUTSIDE REVERSE FOLD**

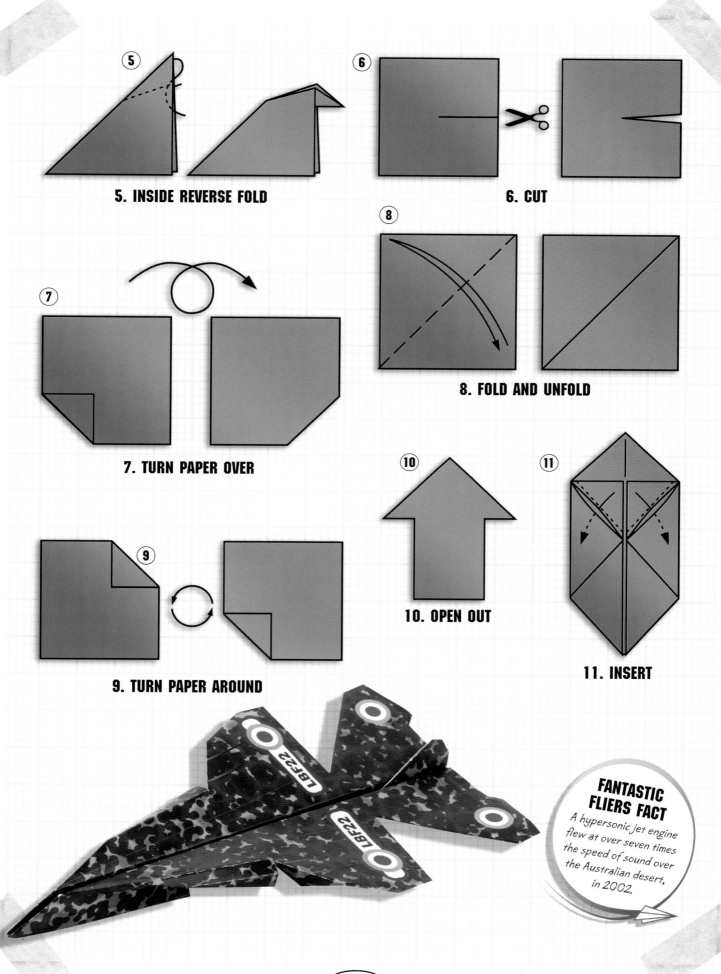

5. INSIDE REVERSE FOLD

6. CUT

7. TURN PAPER OVER

8. FOLD AND UNFOLD

9. TURN PAPER AROUND

10. OPEN OUT

11. INSERT

LBF22
LBF22

FANTASTIC FLIERS FACT
A hypersonic jet engine flew at over seven times the speed of sound over the Australian desert, in 2002.

BAᴇ HUNTER UK

THIS FEARLESS COMBAT FIGHTER IS A MUST ON ANY WAR MISSION.
USE THE PRINTED PAGE NUMBERED 1 AT THE BACK OF THIS SECTION.

①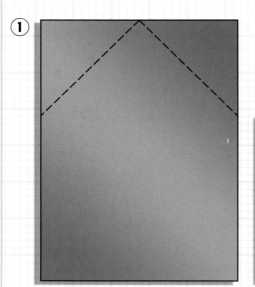

1. Fold in the two top corners along the dotted lines using valley folds.

②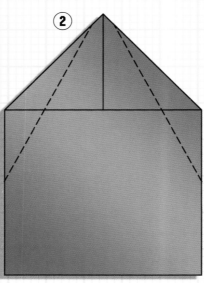

2. Fold along the two diagonal dotted lines, again using valley folds.

③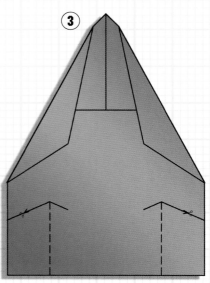

3. Cut along the two solid angled lines, as shown. Now fold in the two flaps, using valley folds, along the dotted lines. Keep these flaps firmly in place throughout the remaining stages.

④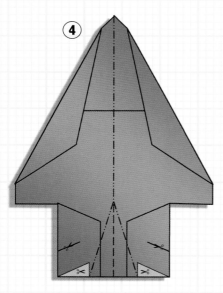

4. Make mountain folds along the three dashed lines running down the center of the plane. Make sure you form a short valley fold between the two diagonal mountain folds at the rear of the plane. Cut away the two rear triangles to shape the tail fins. Cut the two small solid lines.

⑤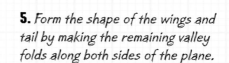

5. Form the shape of the wings and tail by making the remaining valley folds along both sides of the plane.

Hold the base of your plane between your thumb and forefinger and throw quite firmly.

FANTASTIC FLIERS FACT
Modern fighter jets can do amazing things. The MIG 29 can practically stop in mid-air—or shoot straight upwards.

BAe HAWK 200

ANOTHER AMAZING AIRCRAFT MADE IN A FEW EASY STEPS.
USE THE PRINTED PAGE NUMBERED 2 AT THE BACK OF THIS SECTION.

①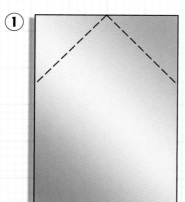
②

1. Fold in the two top corners along the dotted lines using valley folds.

2. Fold down the top triangle along the dotted line using a valley fold. Next, make two mountain folds along the diagonal dashed lines by folding the pointed tip back on itself. Firmly fold the plane down its center, using a valley fold, ensuring that the folds in the pointed tip stay securely tucked in place.

③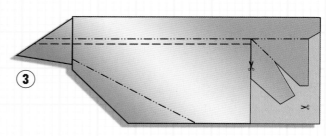

④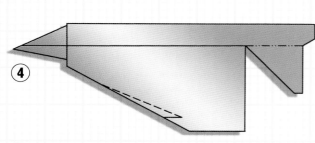

3. Form the tail shape by cutting along the solid lines, as shown. To create the plane's body and wings, bend mountain folds and valley folds along the dotted lines, as shown.

4. Make a cut along the bottom of the wings on the solid line, as shown. Valley fold along the diagonal lines on both sides, to form the wings. Tuck the tail up through the slit at the rear of the plane using a series of inward-facing folds, as shown (right). Bend down the tail fins.

Hold the base of the plane between your thumb and forefinger about 2 inches from the front and gently throw it straight forward.

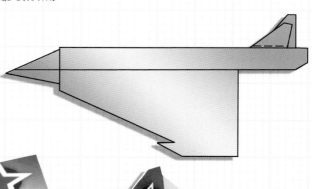

FANTASTIC FLIERS FACT
The Sopwith Camel was one of World War I's greatest fighter aircraft, with around 3,000 combat victories.

BAᴇ HARRIER GR MK7

PREPARE FOR COMBAT WITH THIS GREAT FIGHTER PLANE.
USE THE PRINTED PAGE NUMBERED 3 AT THE BACK OF THIS SECTION.

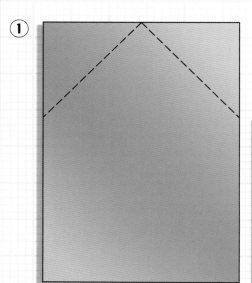

1. Fold in the two top corners along the dotted lines using valley folds.

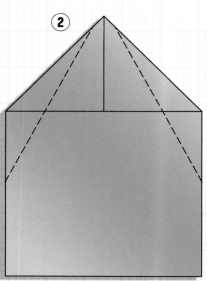

2. Fold along the two diagonal dotted lines, again using valley folds.

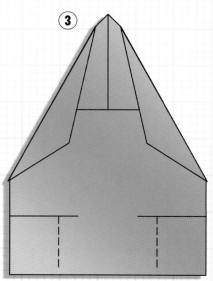

3. Cut along the two short horizontal lines on either side of the plane. Then fold in these tabs along the vertical lines.

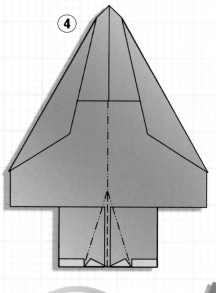

4. Cut along the bottom solid lines to cut a rectangle from the rear of the plane. Make mountain folds along the three dashed lines running down the center of the plane. Make sure you form a short valley fold between the two diagonal mountain folds at the rear of the plane.

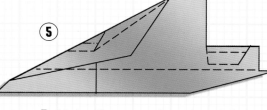

5. Make short cuts along the solid lines on the wing and tail areas. Using valley folds, form the shape of the plane by folding along the lines, as shown.

To fly your plane hold it between your forefinger and thumb about 4 inches from the front, and throw it gently.

FANTASTIC FLIERS FACT

The Spitfire had a hi-tech metal skinned body. Its propeller blades could be set at different angles to help it at takeoff or in high speed flying.

EF-2000

THIS STREAMLINED FIGHTER WILL GLIDE INTO ACTION WITH THE GREATEST OF EASE. USE THE PRINTED PAGE NUMBERED 4 AT THE BACK OF THIS SECTION.

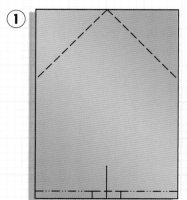

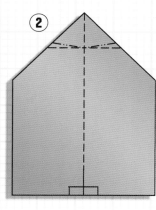

1. Fold in the two top corners along the dotted lines using valley folds. Make three vertical cuts at the bottom along the solid lines. Bend the outside flaps under using mountain folds. Then bend the inside flaps up by using valley folds.

2. Fold down the top triangle using a valley fold. Next, make two mountain folds along the diagonal lines by folding the pointed tip back on itself. Firmly fold the plane down its center, using a valley fold, ensuring that the folds in the pointed tip stay securely tucked in place.

3. Using the solid lines as your guide, cut away the area around the tail of the plane. Make a series of mountain folds and valley folds to form the shape of the plane, as shown. Tuck the tail up through the slit at the rear of the plane using a mountain fold on each side, as shown.

4. Fold up the wing tips using valley folds along the dotted lines. Secure the tail by tucking the flap from one side around the other and interlock them.

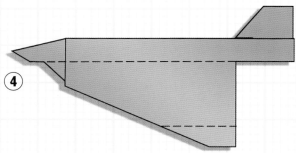

To fly the plane hold it 2 inches from the front and throw it gently forward.

FANTASTIC FLIERS FACT
The P-51 Mustang was a fast and furious fighter. It was also amazing because of its range. It could fly 1,500 miles.

LOCKHEED F-117A

THIS UNUSUAL LOOKING PLANE MAKES A GREAT FIGHTER.
USE THE PRINTED PAGE NUMBERED 5 AT THE BACK OF THIS SECTION.

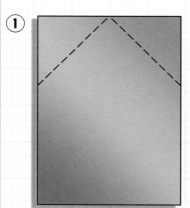 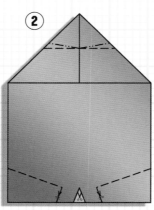 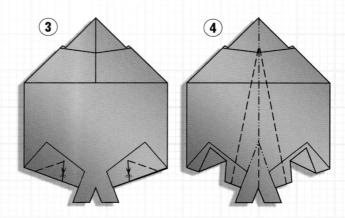

1. *Fold in the two top corners using valley folds.*

2. *Fold down the top triangle using a valley fold. Next, make two mountain folds along the dashed lines by folding the pointed tip back on itself. Cut out the tail using the solid lines as your guide. Valley folds along the diagonal dotted lines form the rear of the wings.*

3. *Cut two slits along the solid lines. Then, using valley folds, bend along the diagonal lines, as shown.*

4. *Firmly fold the plane down its center using a mountain fold, ensuring that the folds in the pointed tip stay securely tucked in place. Make sure you form a short valley fold between the two diagonal mountain folds at the rear. Fold down the wings along the long diagonals.*

5. *To form the main body and wings, use a series of valley and mountain folds as shown. Open out the tail fins.*

To fly your plane, hold it about 2 inches from the front and throw it gently forward.

FANTASTIC FLIERS FACT
The P-51 Mustang could outrun a Spitfire at low level, and fly three times as far.

BAe SEA HARRIER
THIS JUMP JET GETS STRAIGHT OFF THE GROUND.
USE THE PRINTED PAGE NUMBERED 6 AT THE BACK OF THIS SECTION.

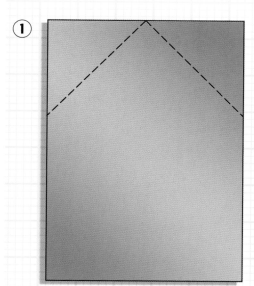

1. Fold in the two top corners along the dotted lines using valley folds.

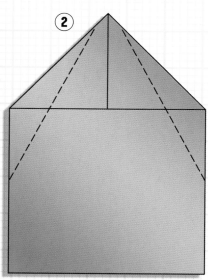

2. Fold along the two diagonal dotted lines, again using valley folds.

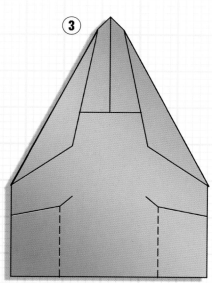

3. Cut two short angled lines along the solid lines on either side. Fold these flaps over using valley folds along the vertical lines, as shown. Make sure these flaps are kept tucked in for all of the following steps.

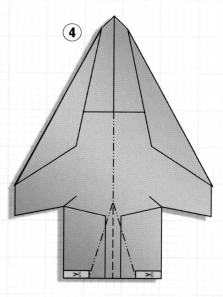

4. Cut out two small rectangles at the bottom by following the solid lines. Make mountain folds along the dashed lines and valley folds along the dotted lines to form the shape of the plane, as shown.

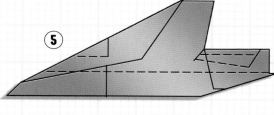

5. Make small slits by cutting along the solid lines on the wings and tail section, as shown. Using valley folds, create the main shape of the body and wings.

To fly your plane hold it about 2 inches from the front and throw it gently forward.

FANTASTIC FLIERS FACT
In the early years of World War II, the Mustang was the only fighter that could fly far enough to accompany bombers to the German capital, Berlin.

PANAVIA TORNADO IDS

THIS SPEEDY FIGHTER CAN BE CREATED IN MINUTES.
USE THE PRINTED PAGE NUMBERED 7 AT THE BACK OF THIS SECTION.

①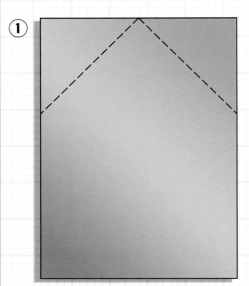

1. Fold in the two top corners along the dotted lines using valley folds.

②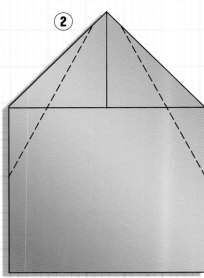

2. Fold along the two diagonal dotted lines, again using valley folds.

③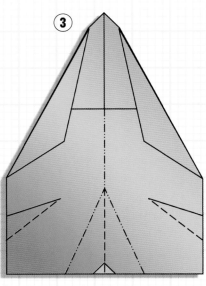

3. Cut along the four solid lines, as shown. Make mountain folds and valley folds to form the shape of the plane.

④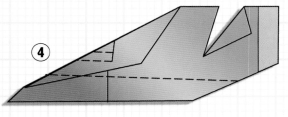

4. Cut off the end of the tail along the solid line. Then cut small slits on the wings along the solid lines, as shown. Using valley folds, form the tail, wings, and body section.

To fly your plane hold it about 4 inches from the front and throw gently forward.

FANTASTIC FLIERS FACT
The P-51 Mustang was an active fighter for over thirty years with air forces around the world.

DASSAULT MIRAGE IVP

MAKE THIS MARVELOUS MIRAGE FIGHTER FOR YOUR MISSIONS.
USE THE PRINTED PAGE NUMBERED 8 AT THE BACK OF THIS SECTION.

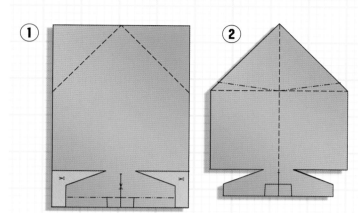

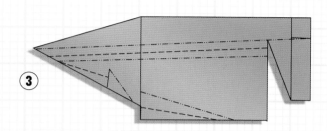

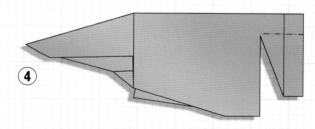

3. Cut a slit toward the front of the wings as indicated by another solid line. Then using a series of valley folds and mountain folds along the edges, form the basic shape of the plane.

1. Fold in the two top corners along the dotted lines using valley folds. Cut three slits at the bottom along the solid lines. Cut away the surplus tail section. Fold the outer flaps under using mountain folds and the inner flaps out using valley folds.

2. Now fold the pointed tip toward you using a valley fold along the straight line. Next, make two mountain folds along the diagonal lines by folding the pointed tip back on itself. Firmly fold the plane down its center, using a valley fold, ensuring that the folds in the pointed tip stay securely tucked in place.

4. Fold up the wing tips using a valley fold and a mountain fold on each wing. Secure the tail by tucking the flap from one side around the other and interlock them.

To fly your plane, hold it about 3 inches from the front and throw it gently forward.

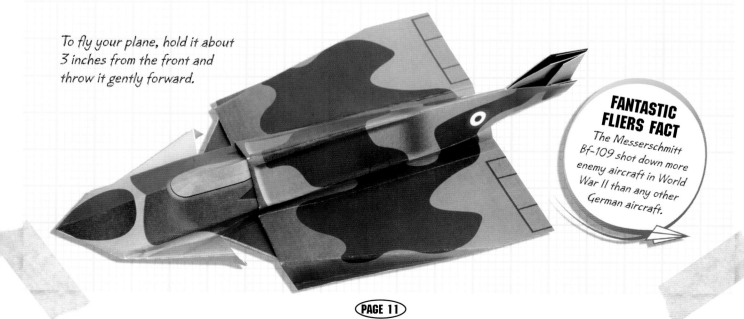

FANTASTIC FLIERS FACT
The Messerschmitt Bf-109 shot down more enemy aircraft in World War II than any other German aircraft.

LOCKHEED BOEING F-22

A GREAT JET FIGHTER MADE IN A FEW EASY STEPS.
USE THE PRINTED PAGE NUMBERED 9 AT THE BACK OF THIS SECTION.

①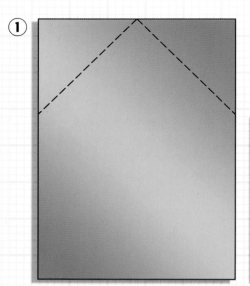

1. Fold in the two top corners along the dotted lines using valley folds.

②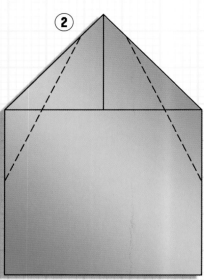

2. Fold along the two diagonal dotted lines, again using valley folds.

③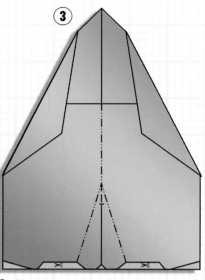

3. First, cut along the vertical solid line at the bottom. Cut away a small part of the tail along the solid lines, as shown. Make mountain folds and valley folds along the lines to form the shape of the plane.

④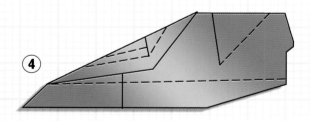

4. Make cuts on the wing along the solid lines. Valley folds along the dotted lines form the basic shape of the plane's body and wings.

FANTASTIC FLIERS FACT

The Fokker Wulf was built for air-to-air combat, and as a fighter bomber. It could carry cannon and machine guns—and up to three 500lb. bombs.

To fly the plane, hold it about 4 inches from the front and throw it gently forward.

MCDONNELL DOUGLAS F-15 EAGLE

THIS BIRD-LIKE PLANE WILL GLIDE WITH EASE.
USE THE PRINTED PAGE NUMBERED 10 AT THE BACK OF THIS SECTION.

①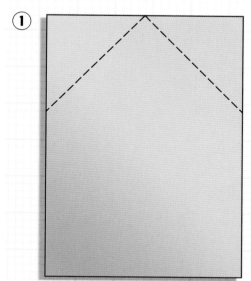

1. Fold in the two top corners along the dotted lines using valley folds.

②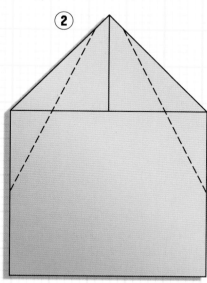

2. Fold along the two diagonal dotted lines, again using valley folds.

③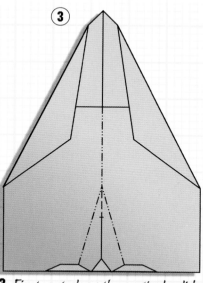

3. First, cut along the vertical solid line at the bottom, as shown. Cut away the tail shape. Firmly fold the plane down its center using a mountain fold. Make sure you form a short valley fold by the slit, between the rear mountain folds.

④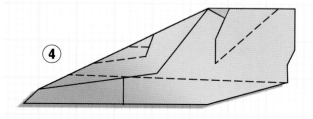

4. Make cuts on the wings along the solid lines, as shown. Using valley folds, fold along the dotted lines to create the shape of the wings.

To fly your plane, hold it about 4 inches from the front and throw it gently forward.

FANTASTIC FLIERS FACT
The Harrier Jump Jet uses swiveling nozzles on its engine to give it vertical lift.

MIG-23 FLOGGER

THIS RUSSIAN PLANE IS GREAT IN A DOGFIGHT.
USE THE PRINTED PAGE NUMBERED 11 AT THE BACK OF THIS SECTION.

①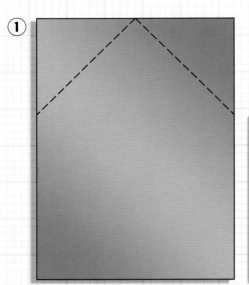

1. Fold in the two top corners along the dotted lines using valley folds.

②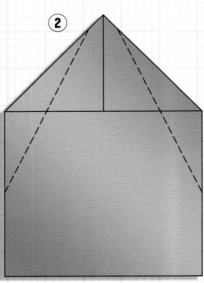

2. Fold along the two diagonal dotted lines, again using valley folds.

③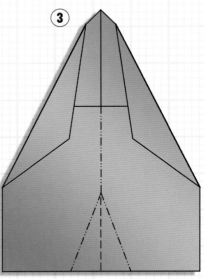

3. Fold the whole plane in two by making mountain folds along the center line and the two small diagonals. Make a valley fold along the bottom section.

④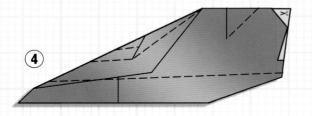

4. Cut away the tail by using the solid lines as a guide. Make cuts on the wings along the solid lines, as shown. Using valley folds, fold along the dotted lines to create the shape of the plane.

FANTASTIC FLIERS FACT
The Phantom F4 often flew from aircraft carriers. It had fold-back wings to take up less space.

To fly your plane, hold it about 4 inches from the front and throw it gently forward.

F-14 TOMCAT

THIS IMPRESSIVE F-14 TOMCAT WILL TEAR THROUGH THE SKY AT TOP SPEED.
USE THE PRINTED PAGE NUMBERED 12 AT THE BACK OF THIS SECTION.

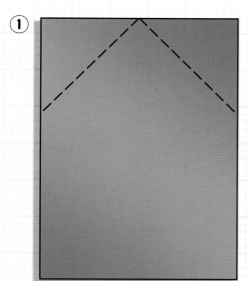

1. Hold the page pattern-side down. Fold the top corners along the dotted lines using valley folds.

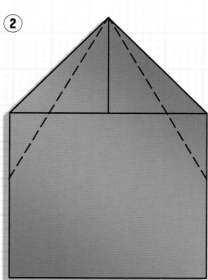

2. Make two more valley folds along the diagonal dotted lines.

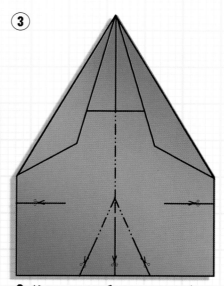

3. Using a pair of scissors, cut along the five solid lines, as shown. Make a mountain fold along the central line running down the plane. Make valley folds on the lines either side of the central fold, making sure you form a short valley fold between the two diagonal mountain folds at the rear of the plane.

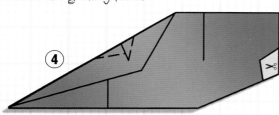

4. Next, cut around the tail area along the solid lines. Now make valley folds along the dotted lines.

5. Using diagonal valley folds, bend the flaps on the tail into place. Then, using more valley folds, form the wings on either side of the plane. Finally, cut the tip off the tail and separate out.

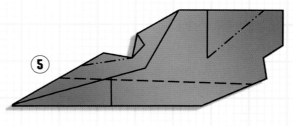

Hold the plane approximately 4 inches from the tip and throw gently.

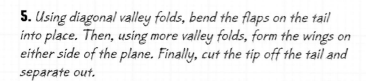

FANTASTIC FLIERS FACT
The P-51 Mustang flew fast, but was built fast, too. It only took 102 days to design and build the first P-51!

SEPECAT JAGUAR

THE SENSATIONAL SEPECAT JAGUAR IS SUPER SPEEDY AND EASY TO MAKE. USE THE PRINTED PAGE NUMBERED 13 AT THE BACK OF THIS SECTION.

①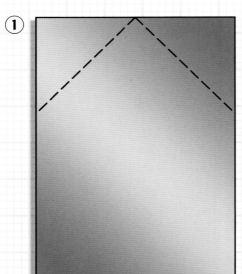

②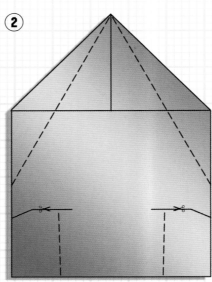

③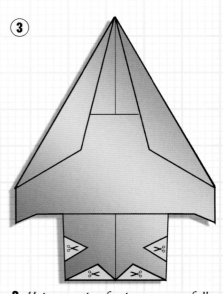

1. Hold the page pattern-side down. Using valley folds, fold the top corners along the dotted lines.

2. Make two more valley folds along the diagonal dotted lines. Using a pair of scissors, carefully cut along the solid lines. Now fold in the two flaps, along the dotted lines.

3. Using a pair of scissors, carefully cut away the four triangles to shape the tail fins.

5. Next form the wings by making the remaining valley folds on both sides of the plane's body. Finish the tail with diagonal folds.

④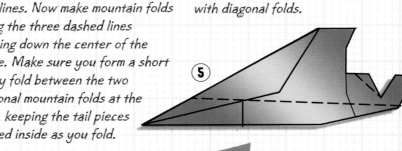

4. Fold in the tail along the vertical fold lines. Now make mountain folds along the three dashed lines running down the center of the plane. Make sure you form a short valley fold between the two diagonal mountain folds at the rear, keeping the tail pieces tucked inside as you fold.

⑤

Grip the underside of your plane, approximately 4 inches from the tip, and throw.

FANTASTIC FLIERS FACT
The Fokker DR.1 had three wings, and in WW1 could outclimb any other plane. It could hide in the sun, and surprise other aircraft from above.

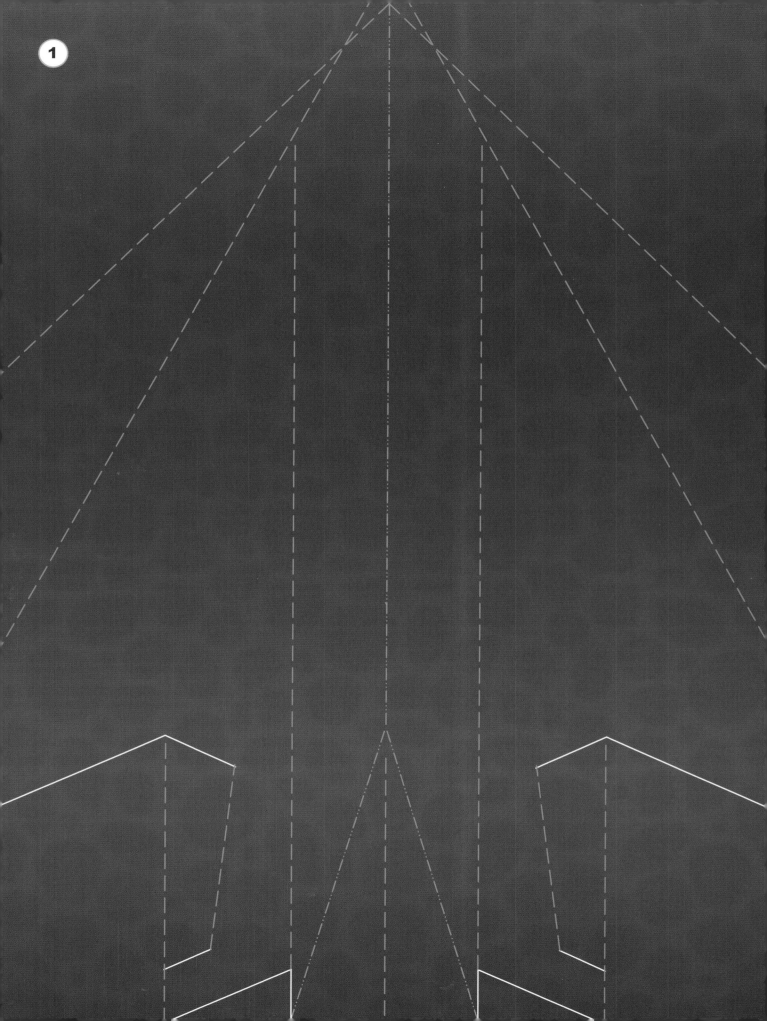

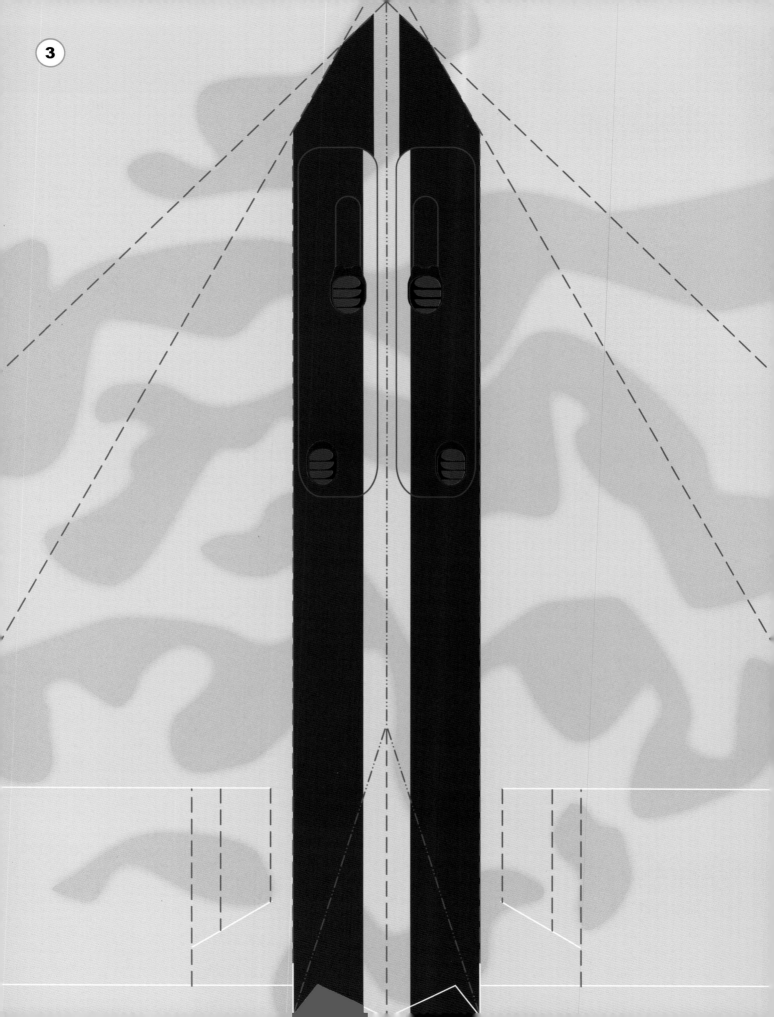

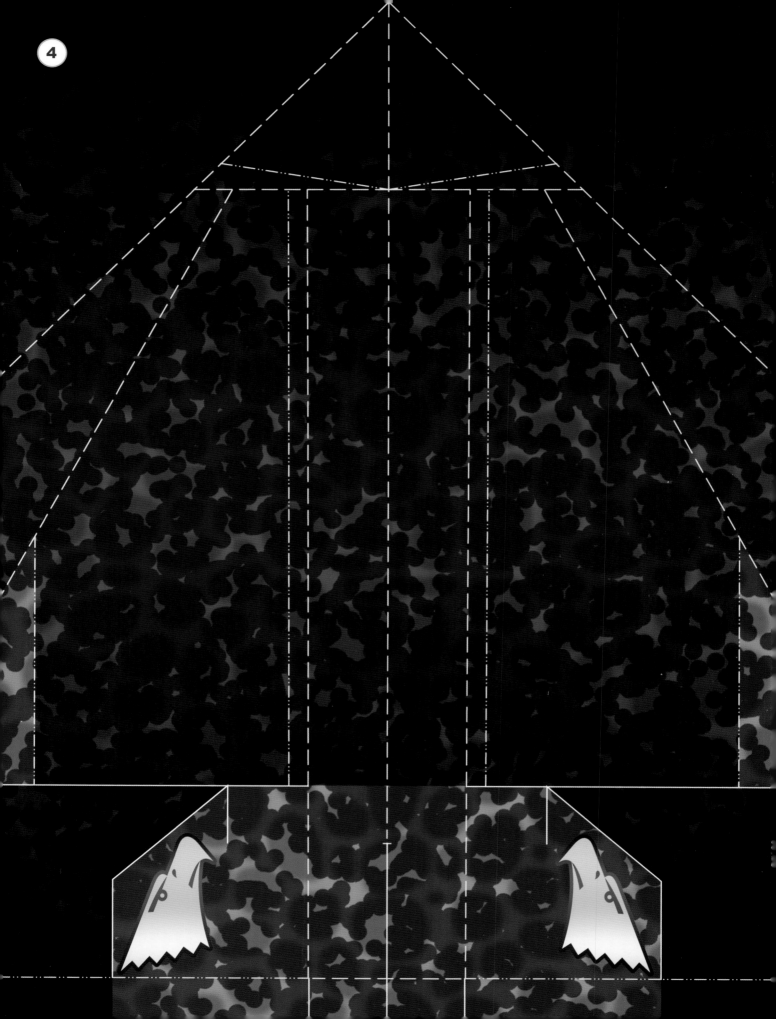

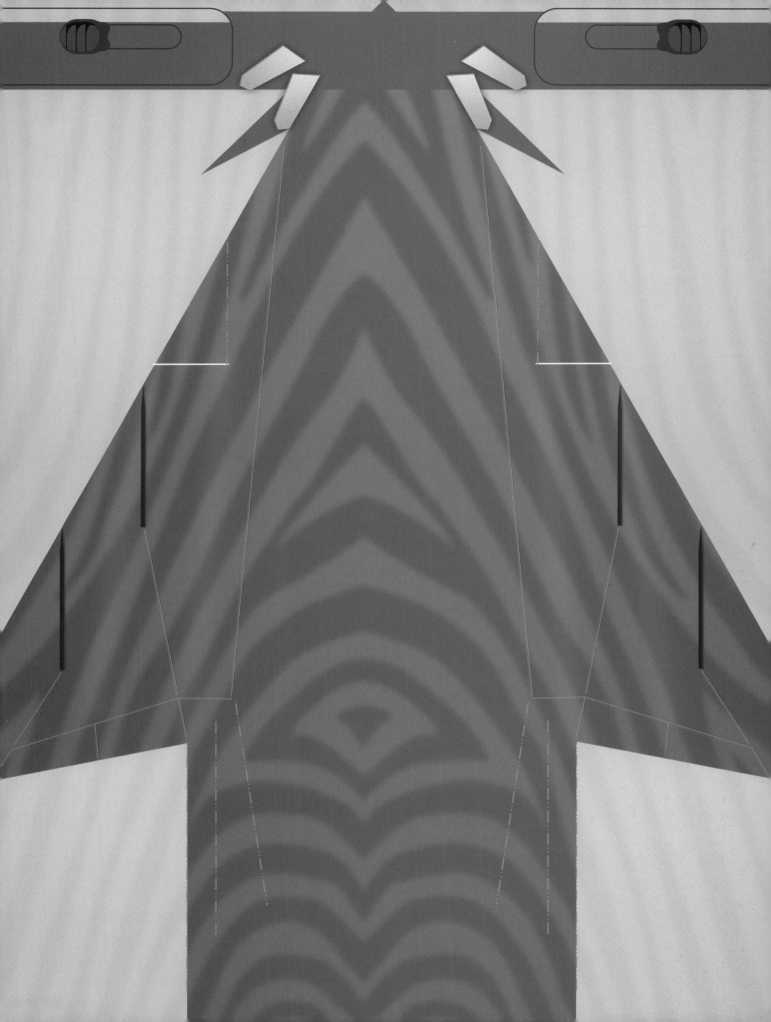

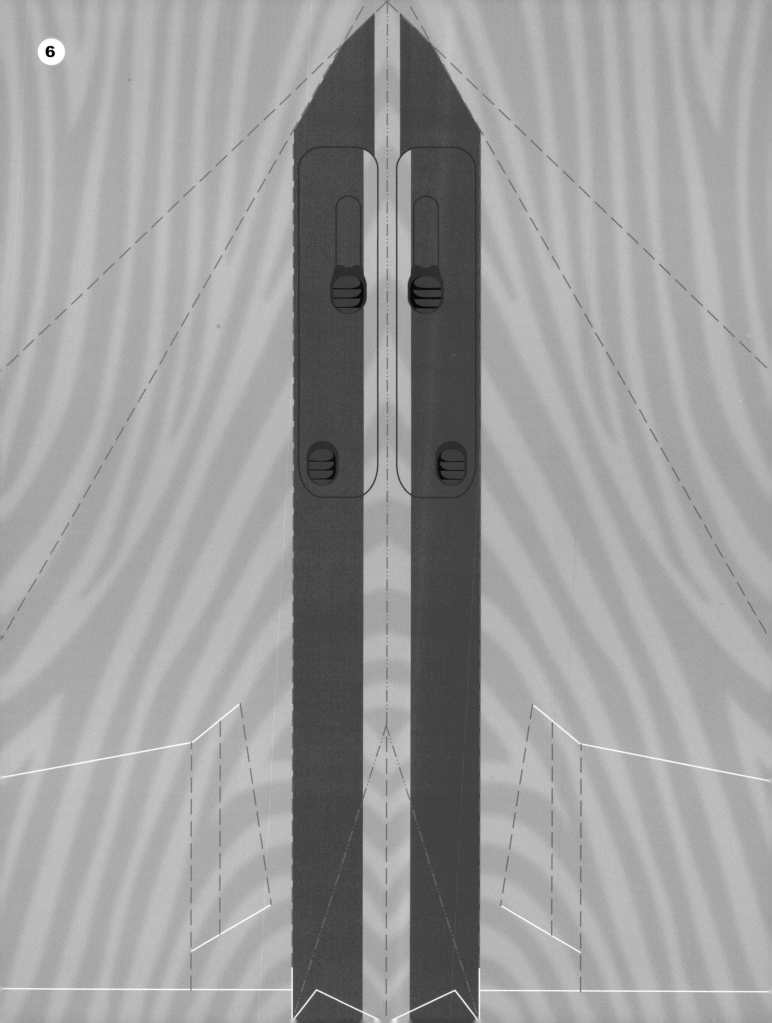

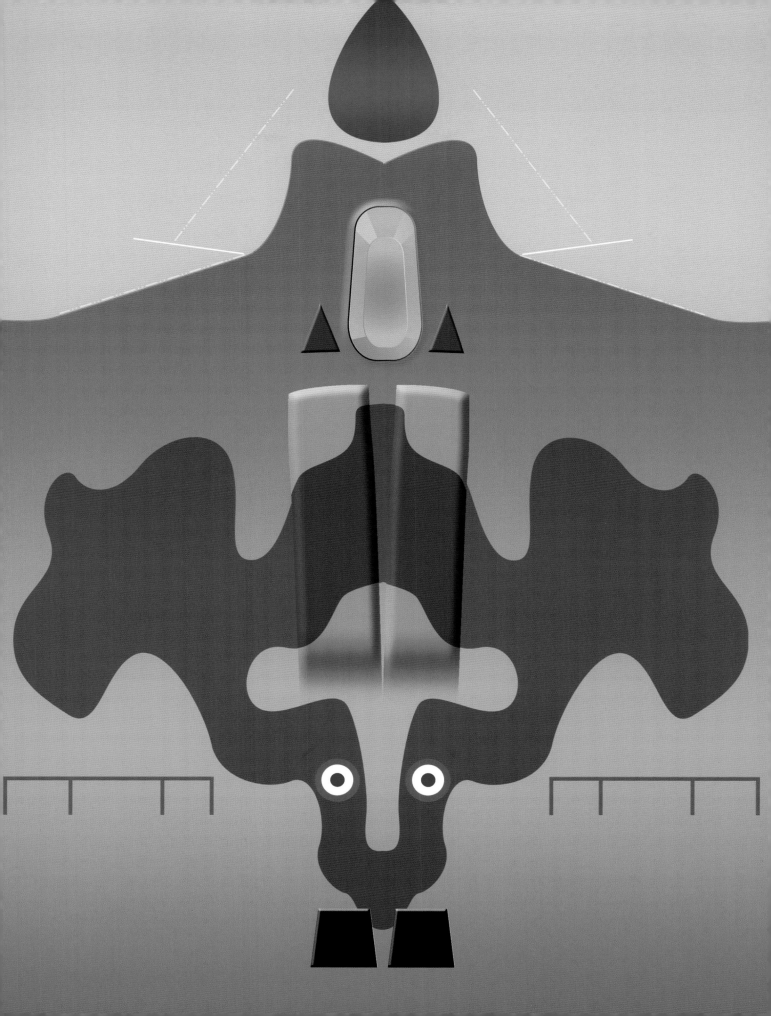

LBF22

LBF22

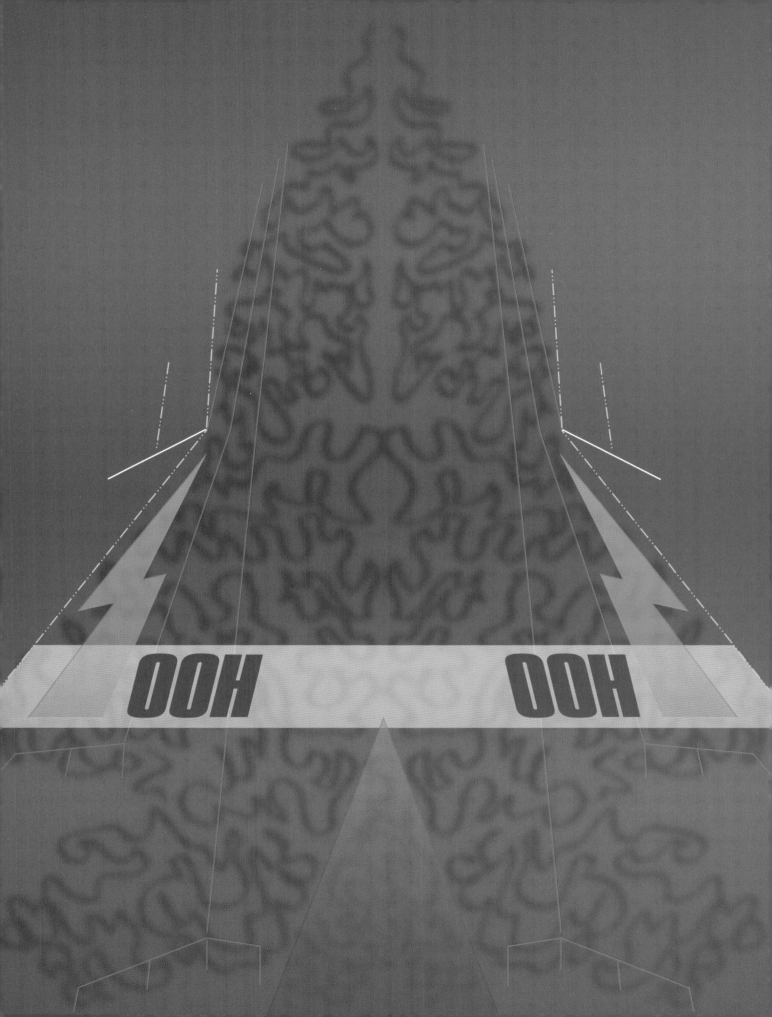

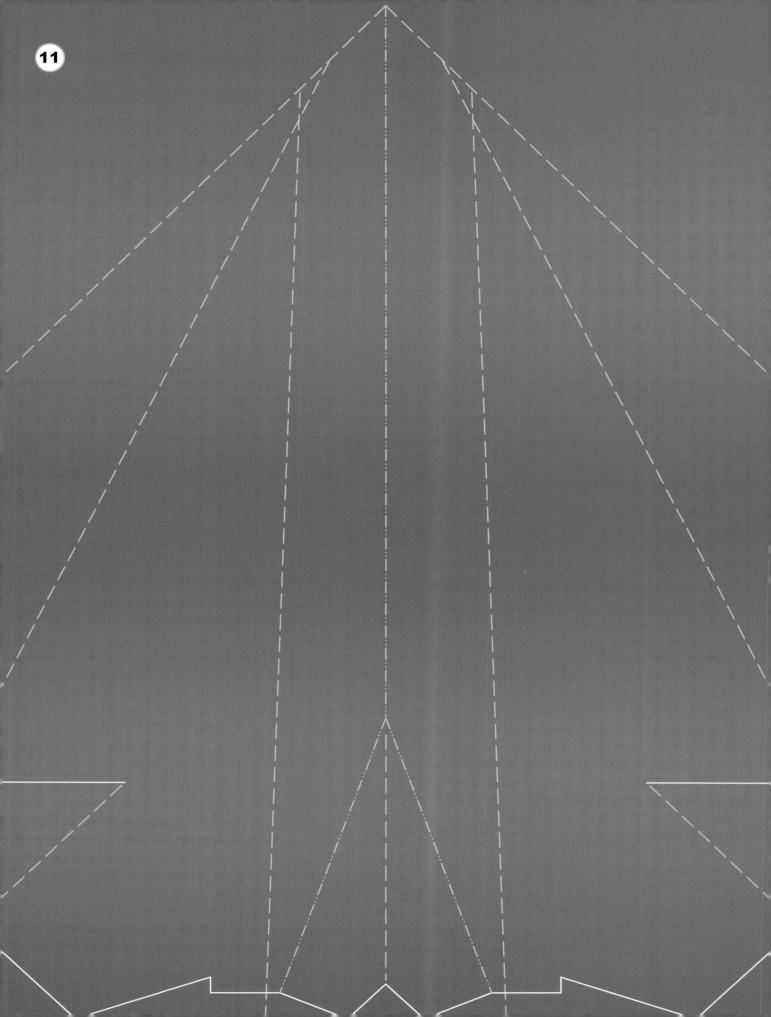

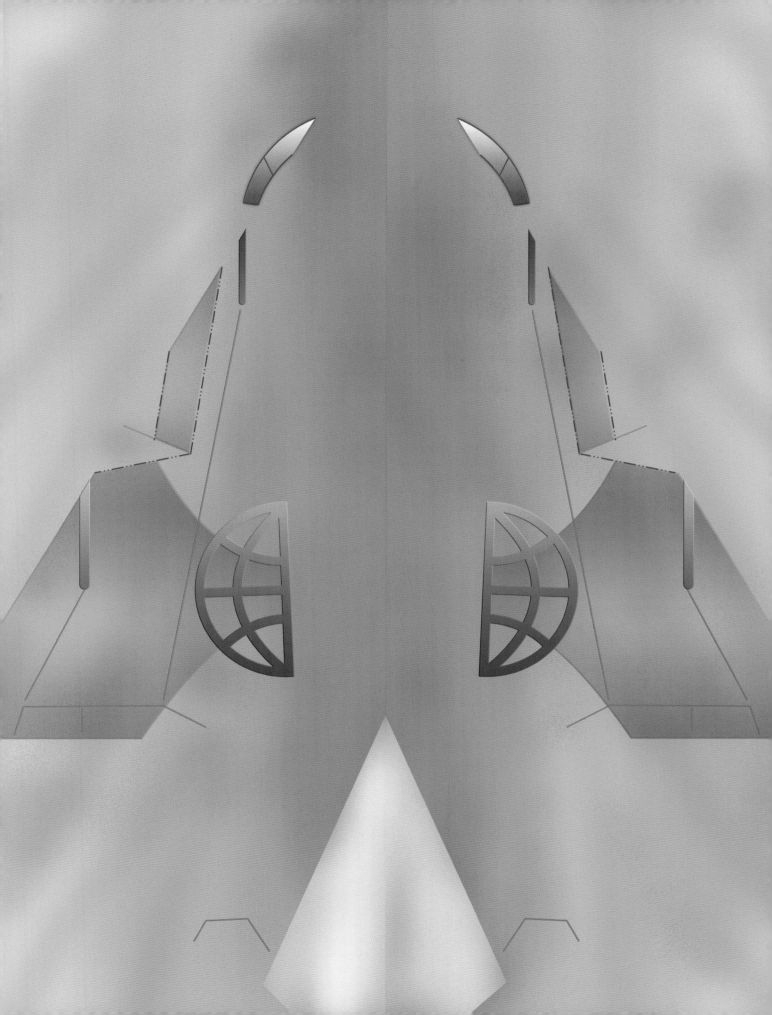

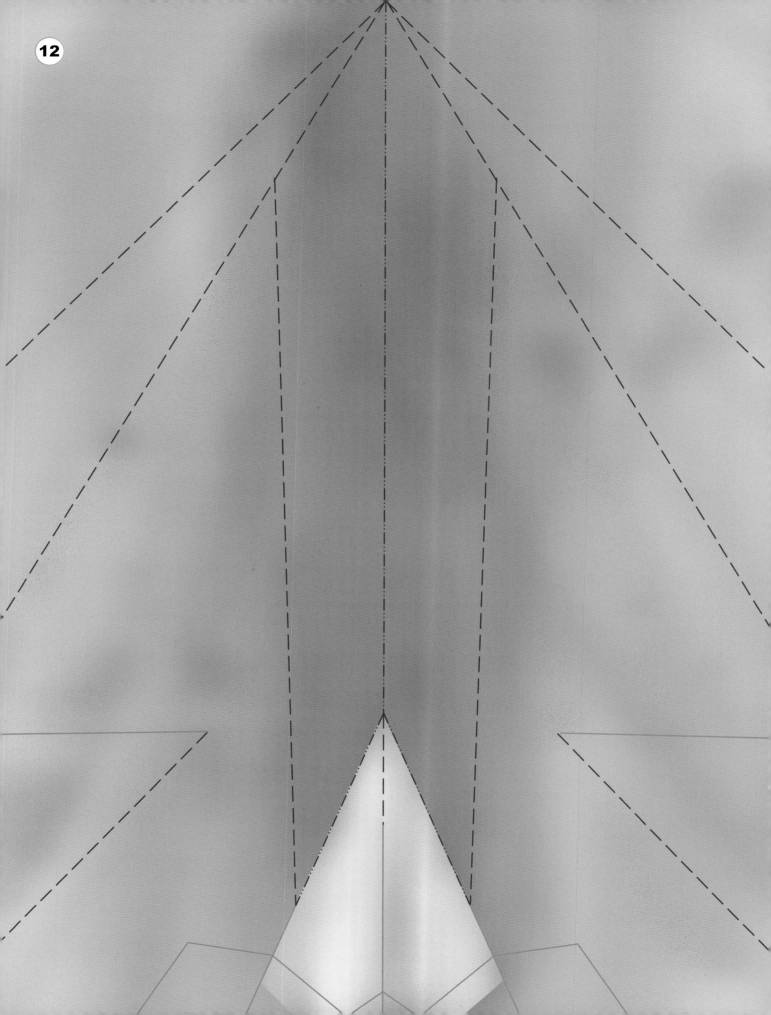

12

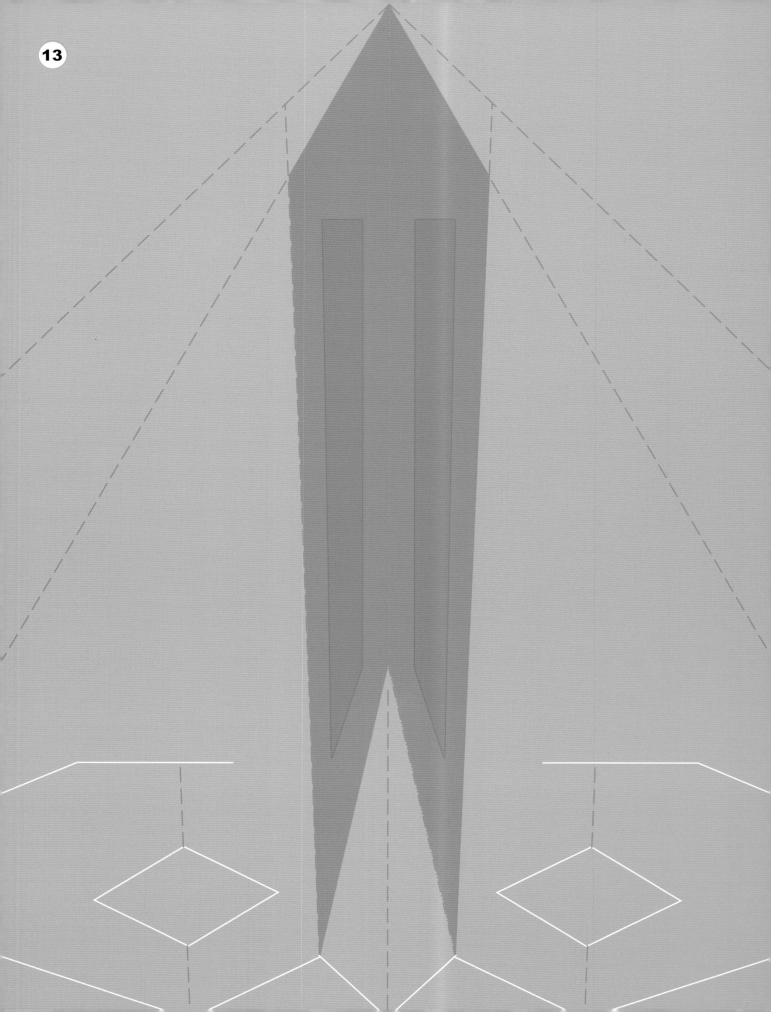

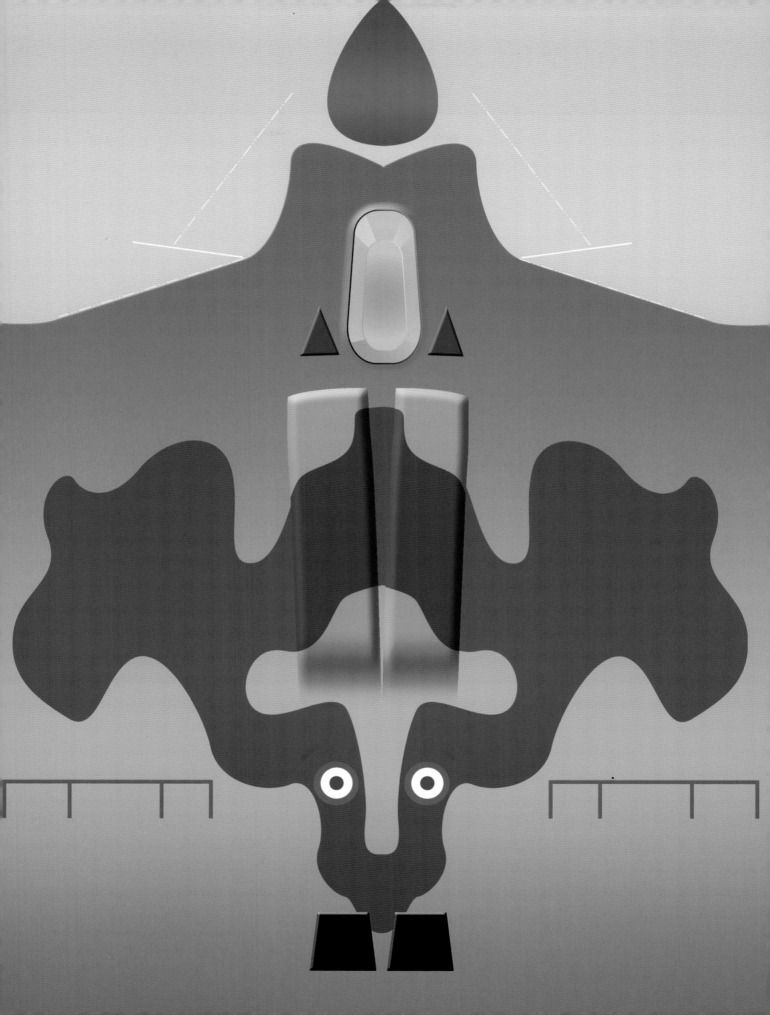

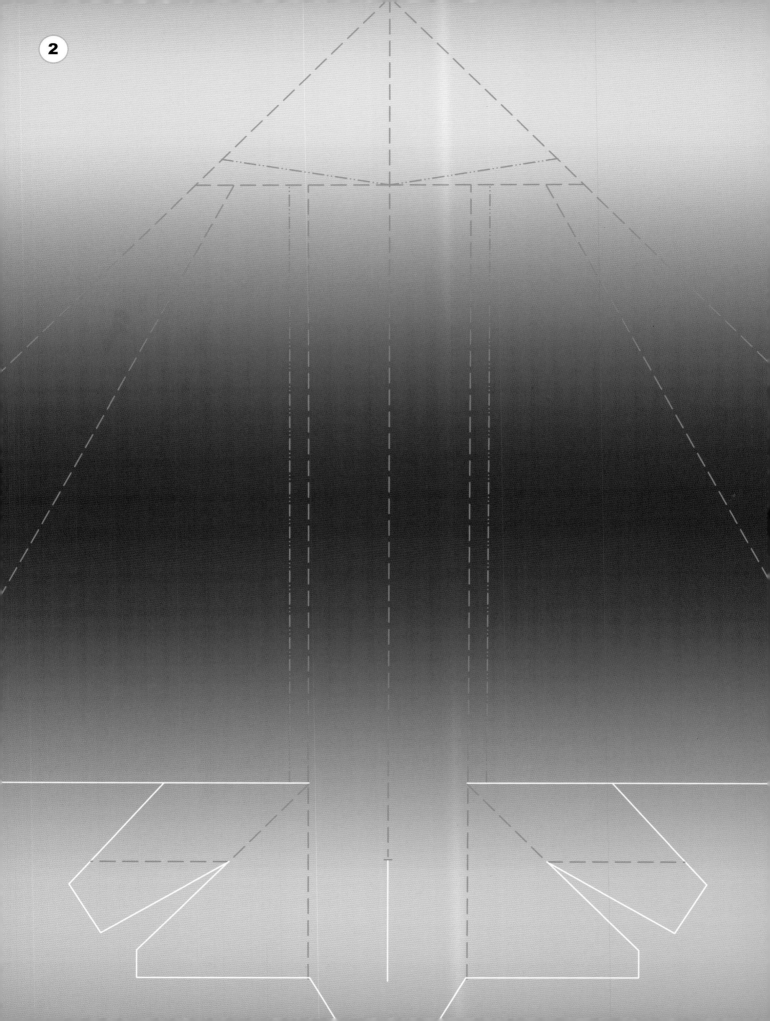

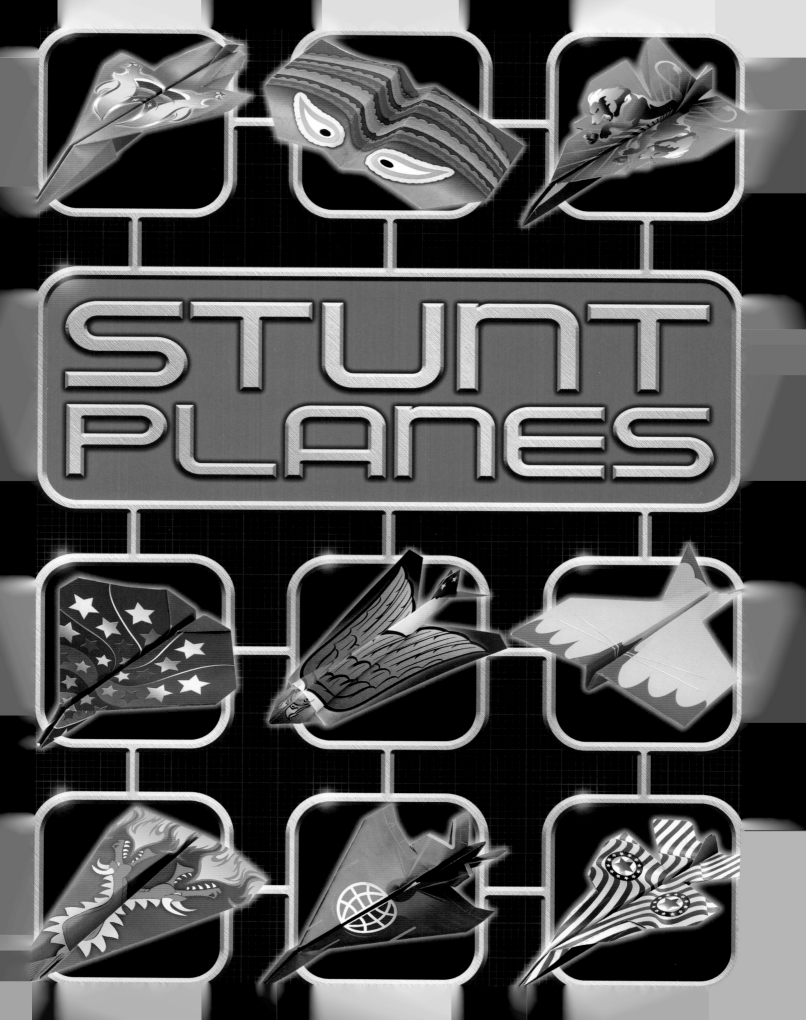

STUNT PLANES

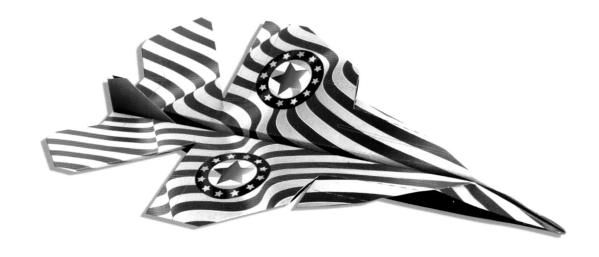

imagine THAT!™

Imagine That! is an imprint of Top That! Publishing plc
27101 Breakers Cove, Valencia, CA 91355
www.topthatpublishing.com

FOLDING TIPS

BEFORE YOU BEGIN ANY OF THE PROJECTS IN THIS SECTION, HERE ARE SOME HELPFUL TIPS THAT WILL MAKE YOUR FOLDING EASIER:

- *Before you start folding, make sure your paper is the correct shape.*

- *Fold on a flat surface, like a table or a book.*

- *Make your folds and cuts neat and accurate.*

- *Crease your folds into place by running your thumbnail along them.*

- *Carefully score along the marked lines using safety scissors and a ruler. This will make folding easier, especially as the lines become obscured toward the end of the model-making.*

SYMBOLS AND BASIC FOLDING PROCEDURES

These symbols show the direction in which paper should be folded. Although you'll not use them all in this section, you can use them to make up your own planes.

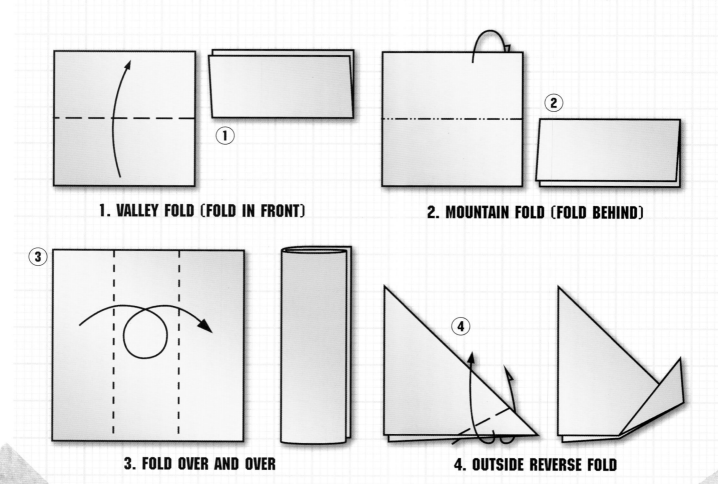

1. VALLEY FOLD (FOLD IN FRONT)

2. MOUNTAIN FOLD (FOLD BEHIND)

3. FOLD OVER AND OVER

4. OUTSIDE REVERSE FOLD

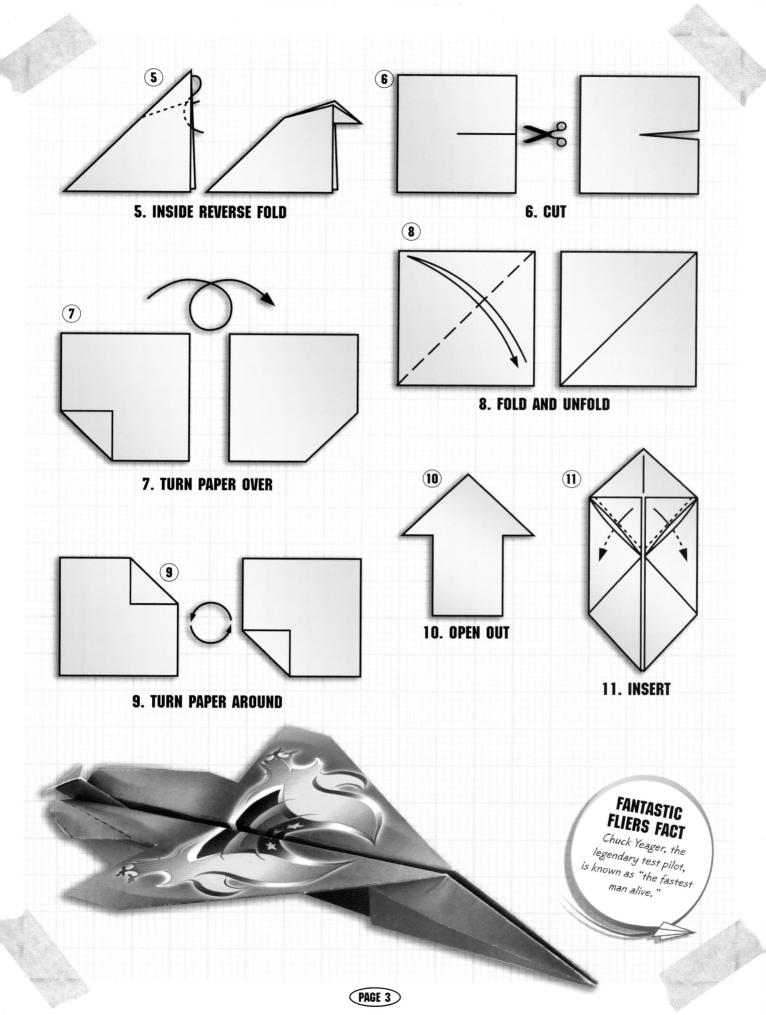

5. INSIDE REVERSE FOLD

6. CUT

7. TURN PAPER OVER

8. FOLD AND UNFOLD

9. TURN PAPER AROUND

10. OPEN OUT

11. INSERT

FANTASTIC FLIERS FACT
Chuck Yeager, the legendary test pilot, is known as "the fastest man alive."

RADICAL ROLLER

MAKE THIS STUNNING BARREL-ROLLING PLANE IN A FEW SIMPLE STEPS.
USE THE PRINTED PAGE NUMBERED 1 AT THE BACK OF THIS SECTION.

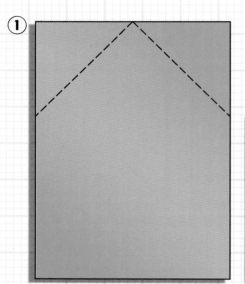

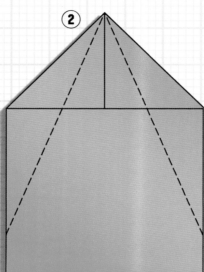

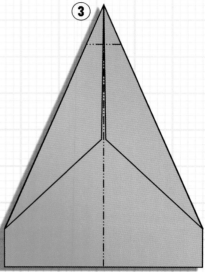

1. Hold the page pattern-side down. Do a valley fold along the right- and left-hand corners along the dotted line, as shown.

2. Using the longer dotted lines as your guide, do another valley fold along the right- and left-hand sides. Make sure you press down firmly to get a neat crease.

3. To form the plane's nose, do a mountain fold along the dashed edge, as shown. Make another mountain fold along the center of the plane. Again, make sure you press firmly enough to make a neat crease.

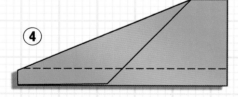

4. Make a valley fold along the body of the plane following the dotted lines as a guide.

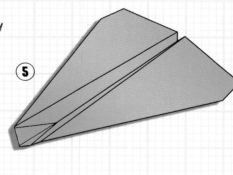

5. Open out the wings making sure they are slightly angled downward, as shown.

To fly your Radical Roller, hold it underneath between your thumb and forefinger about 4 inches from the front, and throw it fast into the air.

FANTASTIC FLIERS FACT
The first display by the British Red Arrows was on May 6th, 1965.

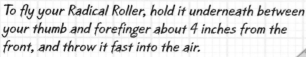

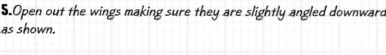

BRILLIANT BOOMERANG

THIS AMAZING STUNT PLANE RETURNS TO BASE ON ITS OWN.
USE THE PRINTED PAGE NUMBERED 2 AT THE BACK OF THIS SECTION.

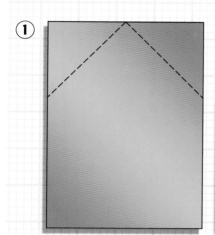

1. Hold the page pattern-side down. Do a valley fold along the right- and left-hand corners along the dotted line as shown.

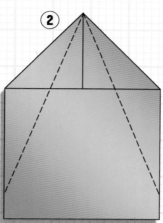

2. Using the longer dotted lines as your guide, do another valley fold along the right- and left-hand sides making sure you press down firmly to get a neat crease.

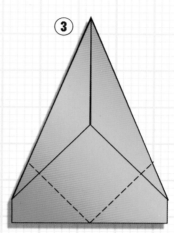

3. Using valley folds, bring the two bottom corners up to form a V-shape.

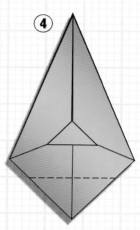

4. Take the bottom V-shape piece and fold down along the dashed line with a mountain fold, as shown.

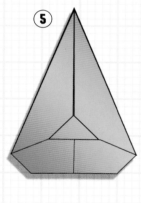

5. Fold the plane in half, using a mountain fold along the center dashed line.

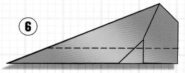

6. Fold the wings along the dotted line, making sure that you adjust their angle upward.

To fly your Brilliant Boomerang, hold it underneath between your forefinger and thumb, about 3 inches from the front. Throw it slowly, and it will curve around in a loop to return to where it began.

FANTASTIC FLIERS FACT
The Canadian Snowbirds stunt team has been seen by over 90 million people in the last 20 years.

LOOPY LOOPER

LOOP THE LOOP WITH THIS CRAZY STUNT MACHINE.
USE THE PRINTED PAGE NUMBERED 3 AT THE BACK OF THIS SECTION.

①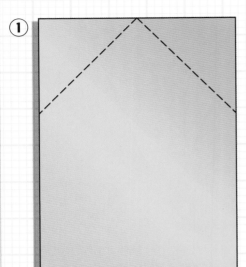

1. Hold the page pattern-side down. Do a valley fold along the right- and left-hand corners along the dotted line as shown.

②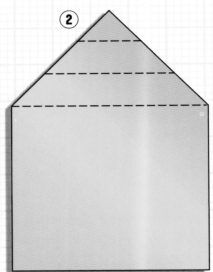

2. Fold down the pointed tip first along the top dotted line, and then along the second dotted line using valley folds. Repeat this along the third dotted line to fold it down farther, as shown.

③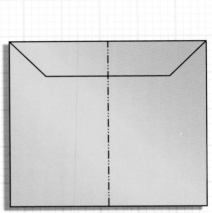

3. Use a mountain fold to fold it down the center along the dashed line, as shown.

④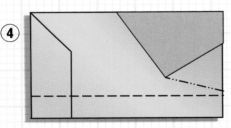

4. Take a pair of scissors and carefully cut along the solid line, making sure to cut through both sides of the plane to make a cut-out V shape. Fold the wings down before folding up the tips at the tail end.

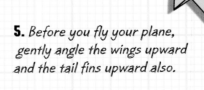

⑤

5. Before you fly your plane, gently angle the wings upward and the tail fins upward also.

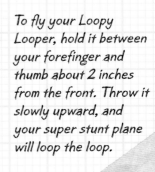

To fly your Loopy Looper, hold it between your forefinger and thumb about 2 inches from the front. Throw it slowly upward, and your super stunt plane will loop the loop.

DARING DART

THIS FAST AND FURIOUS DART-LIKE PLANE WILL STREAK THROUGH THE AIR LIKE LIGHTNING. USE THE PRINTED PAGE NUMBERED 4 AT THE BACK OF THIS SECTION.

①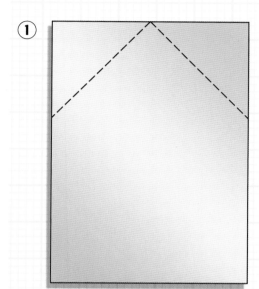

②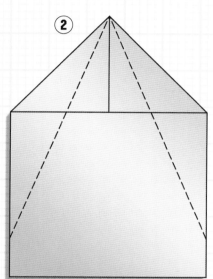

③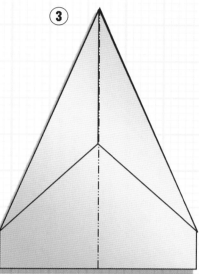

1. Hold the page pattern-side down. Do a valley fold along the right- and left-hand corners along the dotted line as shown.

2. Using the longer dotted lines as your guide, do another valley fold along the right- and left-hand sides. Make sure you press down firmly to get a neat crease.

3. Using a mountain fold, fold the plane in half along the center dashed line.

4. To form the wings, valley fold both the left- and right-hand side of the plane along the long dashed lines, as shown. Remember to press firmly to ensure a neatly creased edge.

④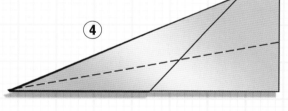

5. Do a valley fold on the wing tips along the dotted lines.

⑤

To fly your Daring Dart, hold it between your forefinger and thumb about 5 inches from the front. Holding it at shoulder height, throw it fast and straight.

FANTASTIC FLIERS FACT
The Blue Angels were named after a famous nightclub in New York.

SUPER SPINNER

THIS SUPER SPINNING STUNT PLANE WOULD MAKE ANY PILOT DIZZY. USE THE PRINTED PAGE NUMBERED 5 AT THE BACK OF THIS SECTION.

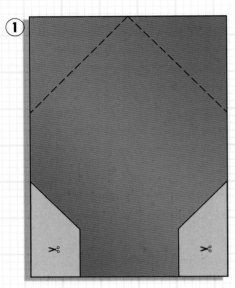

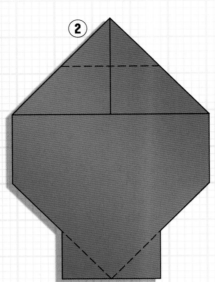

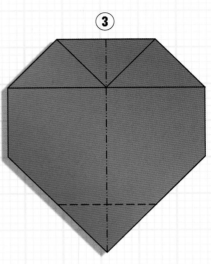

1. Hold the page pattern-side down. Do a valley fold along the right- and left-hand corners along the dotted line as shown. Use a pair of scissors to carefully cut out the bottom corners along the solid line.

2. Take the top pointed edge and make a valley fold along the dotted line, as shown. Then do another two valley folds along the bottom dotted lines to form a V shape.

3. Take the bottom V-shaped piece and, using a mountain fold along the dashed line, turn it behind the body. Then fold the plane along the center dashed line using a mountain fold.

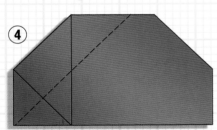

4. Create the pointed nose end by folding each side with a valley fold along the dotted lines, as shown. Make sure you press firmly to create a neatly creased edge

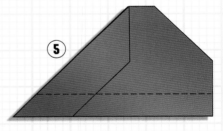

5. To make the wings, fold down each side along the dotted line using a valley fold. Again, press firmly to create a neat edge.

6. Before flying your plane, adjust the wings up slightly.

To fly your plane, hold it between your thumb and forefinger about 4 inches from the front. Throw it quite fast and high to make it perform a spiral-like spin before gently gliding to the ground.

FANTASTIC FLIERS FACT

The most helicopter spins in the skysurfing position is 64 in 20 seconds by Englishman Chris Gauge; in 1999.

STUNT SPINNER

THIS AMAZING PLANE PERFORMS SOME STUNNING SPINS.
USE THE PRINTED PAGE NUMBERED 6 AT THE BACK OF THIS SECTION.

①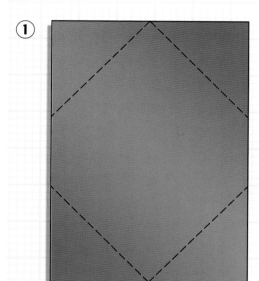

1. Hold the page pattern-side down. Do a valley fold along the right- and left-hand corners along the dotted line as shown.

②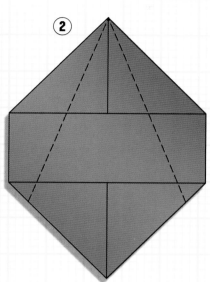

2. Fold in the outer edges along the dotted line to form two valley folds.

③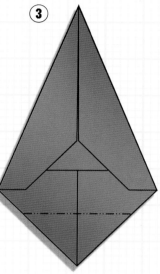

3. Take the pointed tip and fold it back on itself in a mountain fold.

4. Fold the plane in half along the center dashed line using a mountain fold.

5. Fold down the wings using a valley fold on each side.

④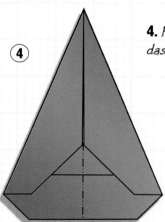

⑤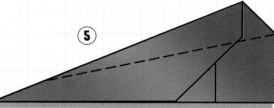

To fly your model, hold it at the tail end. Throw it high up and gently. Watch it spin!

FANTASTIC FLIERS FACT
The Blue Angels fly six F/A-18 Hornets in formation.

SUPER SWOOPER

THIS INCREDIBLE BIRD-LIKE PLANE SWOOPS AND CLIMBS.
USE THE PRINTED PAGE NUMBERED 7 AT THE BACK OF THIS SECTION.

①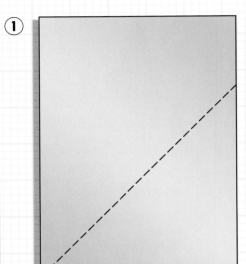

1. Hold the page pattern-side down. Take the bottom right-hand corner and fold it diagonally upward in a valley fold, as shown.

 ②

2. Fold the bottom left-hand corner point upward in a valley fold to create a large V shape.

③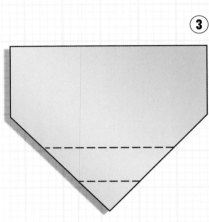

3. Take the bottom point and fold it upward along the bottom dotted line in a valley fold. Now, make a valley fold on the second dotted line. As you bring up the second fold, gently tuck in the small triangle-shaped tip into the back pocket.

④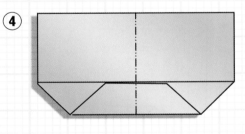

4. Fold the plane in half by making a mountain fold along the center dotted line. Make sure that you press firmly to create a neat edge.

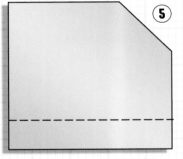 ⑤

5. Make the two wings by using valley folds to bring down the right- and left-hand sides. Again, press firmly on the edges.

Before you fly your Super Swooper, angle the wings slightly upward. Hold it about 2 inches from the front and throw it gently angled downward.

FANTASTIC FLIERS FACT

Stunt maneuvers include loops, figure-of-eights, rolls, and tail slides.

BARREL ROLL BEAUTY

THIS PLANE IS SUPER SPEEDY AND YET SIMPLE TO MAKE!
USE THE PRINTED PAGE NUMBERED 8 AT THE BACK OF THIS SECTION.

①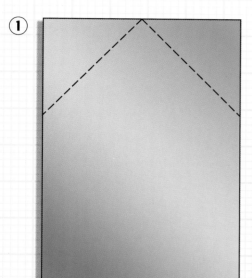

1. Hold the page pattern-side down. Using valley folds, bend in the two top corners.

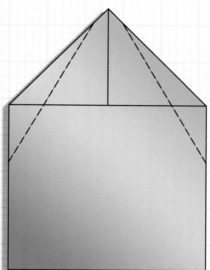

2. Make two valley folds along the diagonal dotted lines.

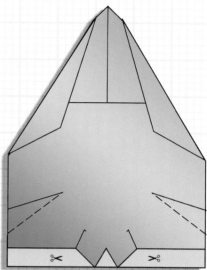

3. Using a pair of scissors, carefully cut along the solid lines to begin forming the wings and tail shape. Below the top set of slits, make two diagonal valley folds to create the side tail fins.

④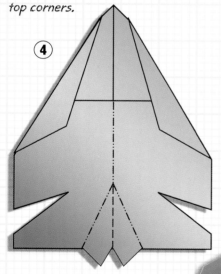

4. Make a mountain fold along the dashed line running down the center of the plane, then two valley folds either side of this line. Fold the wings over. Then form a short valley fold between the two diagonal mountain folds at the rear of the plane.

⑤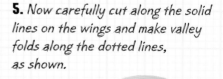

5. Now carefully cut along the solid lines on the wings and make valley folds along the dotted lines, as shown.

Throw the plane gently, holding it approximately 5 inches from the tip.

FANTASTIC FLIERS FACT
Capable of flying at Mach 2, the YF-22 Raptor is one of the fastest planes.

SPIRALING STRIKE FIGHTER

MAKE THIS STUNNING STRIKE FIGHTER IN MINUTES.
USE THE PRINTED PAGE NUMBERED 9 AT THE BACK OF THIS SECTION.

①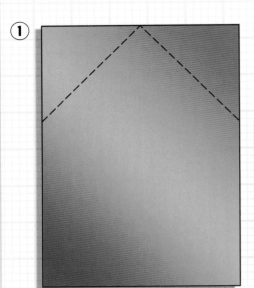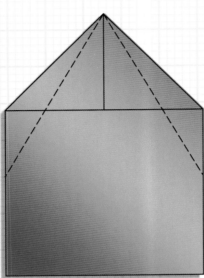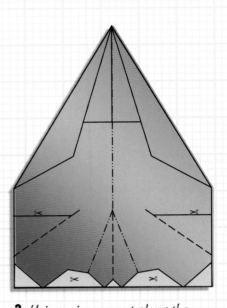

1. Hold the page pattern-side down. Using valley folds, fold in the top two corners.

2. Make two more valley folds along the two diagonal dotted lines.

3. Using scissors, cut along the solid lines around the tail and wings. Make a mountain fold along the dashed line running down the center of the plane. Form a short valley fold between the two diagonal mountain folds at the rear of the plane. Now make horizontal cuts on each rear wing and fold the flaps under each slit along the dotted lines as shown.

④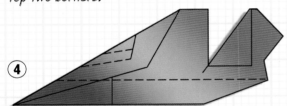

4. Make valley folds along the dotted lines on the wings, as shown. Cut along the diagonal solid lines. Using more valley folds, form the front wings on either side of the plane.

Throw the plane gently, holding it approximately 4 inches from the tip.

FANTASTIC FLIERS FACT
In the movie "Octopussy," a 12-foot long Bede Acrostar jet is used by James Bond to evade a heat-seeking missile.

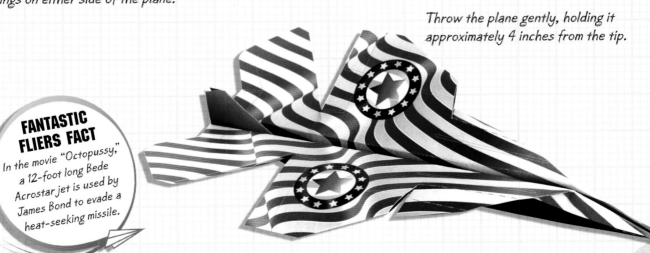

NIFTY NOSEDIVER

FOLLOW THESE EASY STEPS AND SEE YOUR SUPERSONIC JET FLY!
USE THE PRINTED PAGE NUMBERED 10 AT THE BACK OF THIS SECTION.

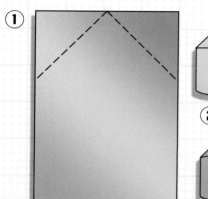

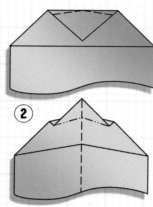

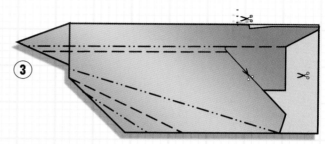

1. Hold the page pattern-side down. Fold in the top two corners using valley folds.

2. Now fold the pointed tip toward you using a valley fold along the straight dotted line. Next, make two mountain folds along the diagonal dashed lines by folding the pointed tip back on itself. Firmly fold the plane down its center, using a valley fold, ensuring that the folds in the pointed tip stay securely tucked in place.

5. Finally, bend down the tail fins using diagonal valley folds to create your finished plane.

Holding your plane approximately 2 inches from the tip of the nose cone, pinch the underside of the wings together and allow your jet to gently glide out of your hand.

3. Using a pair of scissors, carefully cut out the tail and wing shapes using the solid lines as a guide. Make the valley and mountain folds on both sides of the plane's body as indicated by the dotted and dashed lines. Now, make the valley and mountain folds on both wing sections in the same way.

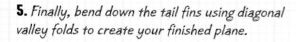

4. Next, using two more mountain folds, bend the tail into shape along the dashed lines and back up through the tail.

FANTASTIC FLIERS FACT
The F-16 Thunderbird team's most famous formation is the flying diamond.

ASTOUNDING U-TURNER

THIS PLANE IS FULL OF CUNNING MANEUVERS—WHY NOT TAKE IT FOR A SPIN?
USE THE PRINTED PAGE NUMBERED 11 AT THE BACK OF THIS SECTION.

①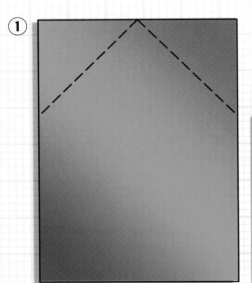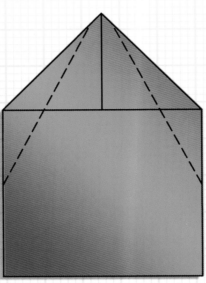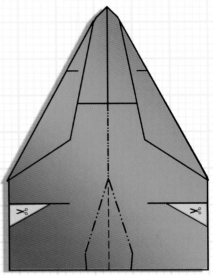

1. Hold the page pattern-side down. Using valley folds, fold the top corners along the dotted lines.

2. Make two more valley folds along the diagonal dotted lines.

3. Cut along all the solid lines around the wing area as shown. Then, make a mountain fold along the dashed line running down the center of the plane. Form a short valley fold between the two diagonal mountain folds at the rear.

④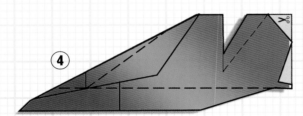

4. Next, cut along the solid lines around the tail area. Form the wings and tail fins by making the remaining valley folds on both sides of the plane's body as indicated by the dotted lines.

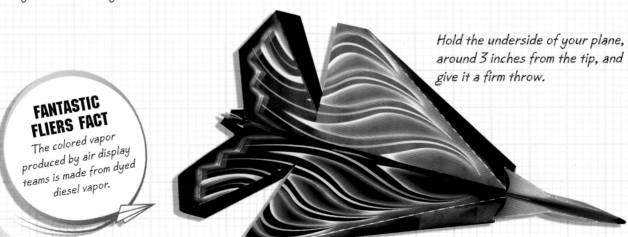

Hold the underside of your plane, around 3 inches from the tip, and give it a firm throw.

FANTASTIC FLIERS FACT
The colored vapor produced by air display teams is made from dyed diesel vapor.

WHIZZING WEAVER

THE SENSATIONAL JET IS SUPER SPEEDY AND EASY TO MAKE.
USE THE PRINTED PAGE NUMBERED 12 AT THE BACK OF THIS SECTION.

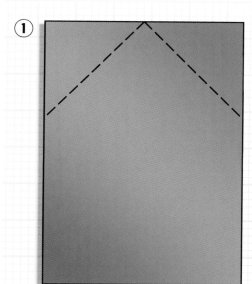

1. Hold the page pattern-side down. Using valley folds, fold the top corners along the dotted lines.

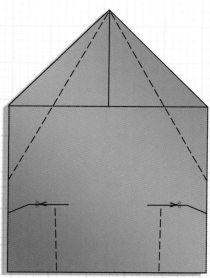

2. Make two more valley folds along the diagonal dotted lines. Using a pair of scissors, carefully cut along the solid lines. Now fold in the two flaps along the dotted lines.

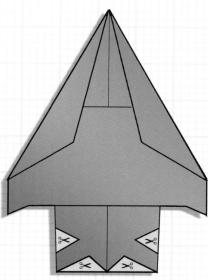

3. Using a pair of scissors, carefully cut away the four triangles to shape the tail fins.

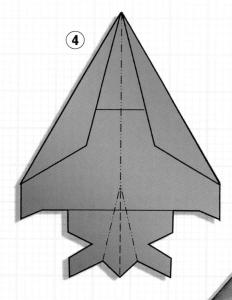

4. Fold in the tail along the vertical fold lines. Now make mountain folds along the three dashed lines running down the center of the plane. Make sure you form a short valley fold between the two diagonal mountain folds at the rear, keeping the tail pieces tucked inside as you fold.

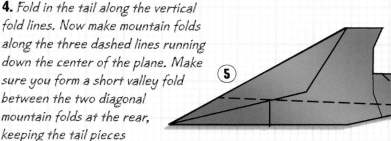

5. Next form the wings by making the remaining valley folds on both sides of the plane's body. Finish the tail with diagonal folds.

Grip the underside of your plane, approximately 4 inches from the tip, and throw.

FANTASTIC FLIERS FACT
The world's only jet-powered biplane was piloted by Jimmy Franklin, who walked on its wings.

CRAZY LOOPER

MAKE THIS CRAZY LOOPER PLANE IN FIVE SIMPLE STAGES.
USE THE PRINTED PAGE NUMBERED 13 AT THE BACK OF THIS SECTION.

①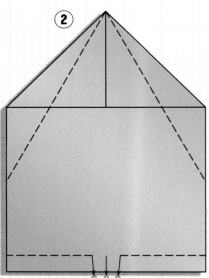

②

③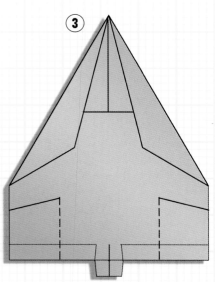

1. *Hold the page pattern-side down. Fold the two top corners toward you using valley folds along the dotted lines.*

2. *Using valley folds, fold along the diagonal dotted lines. Now, using a pair of scissors, carefully cut along the three solid lines as shown, and fold along the horizontal dotted lines on either side of the cuts.*

3. *Now cut along the diagonal solid lines to help form a wing shape. Below the cuts, make two vertical valley folds and keep these flaps firmly folded in for the remaining stages.*

④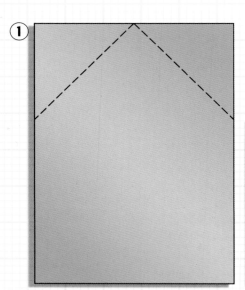

4. *Make a valley fold along the dashed line running down the center of the plane. Form a short valley fold between the two diagonal folds at the rear of the plane.*

⑤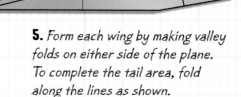

5. *Form each wing by making valley folds on either side of the plane. To complete the tail area, fold along the lines as shown.*

Hold the plane between your thumb and forefinger, approximately 3 inches from the tip, and throw it firmly.

FANTASTIC FLIERS FACT
In 1941, the W1, designed by Frank Whittle, became the first turbojet to fly in Britain.

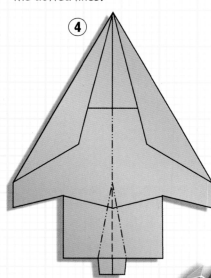

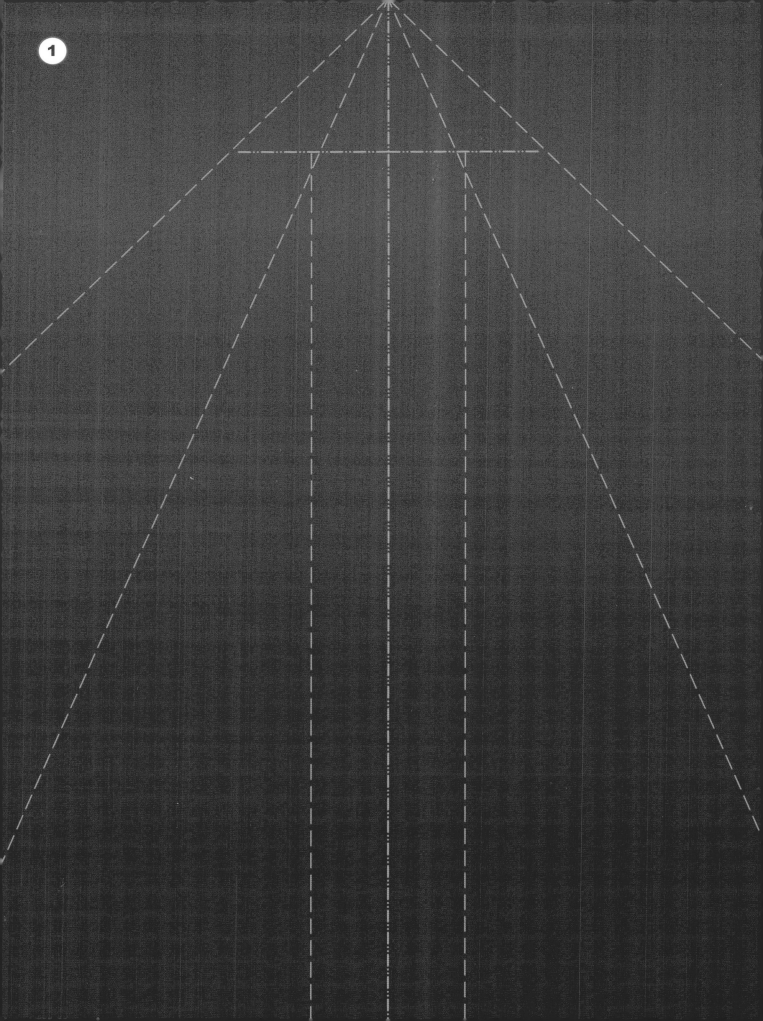

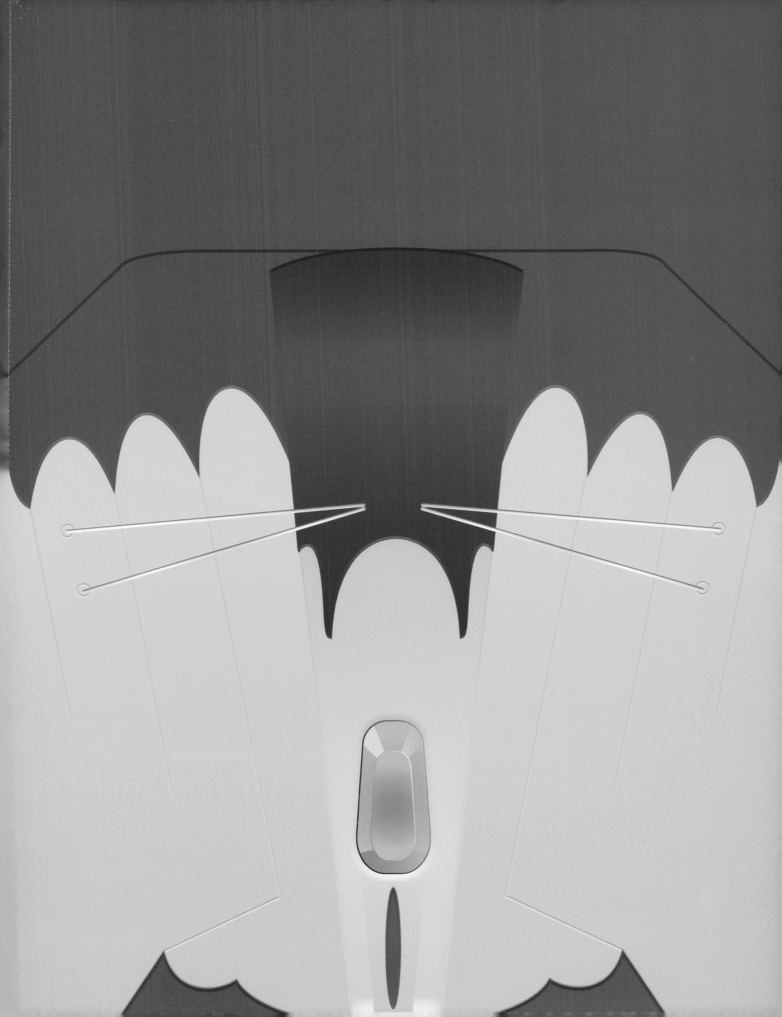

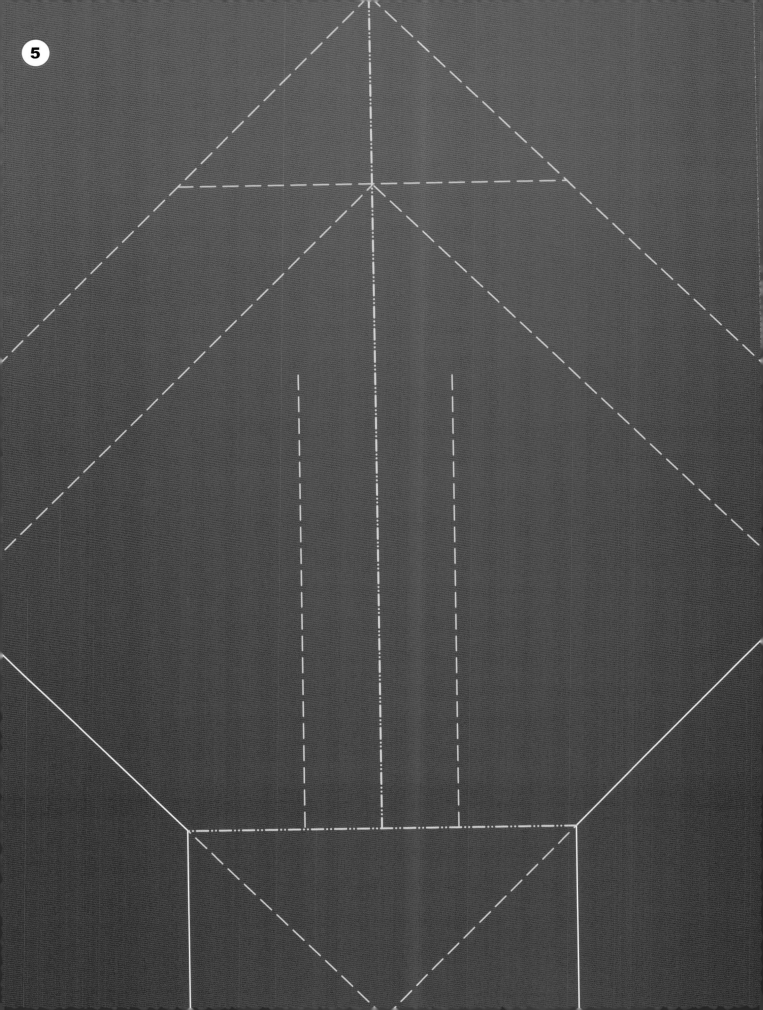

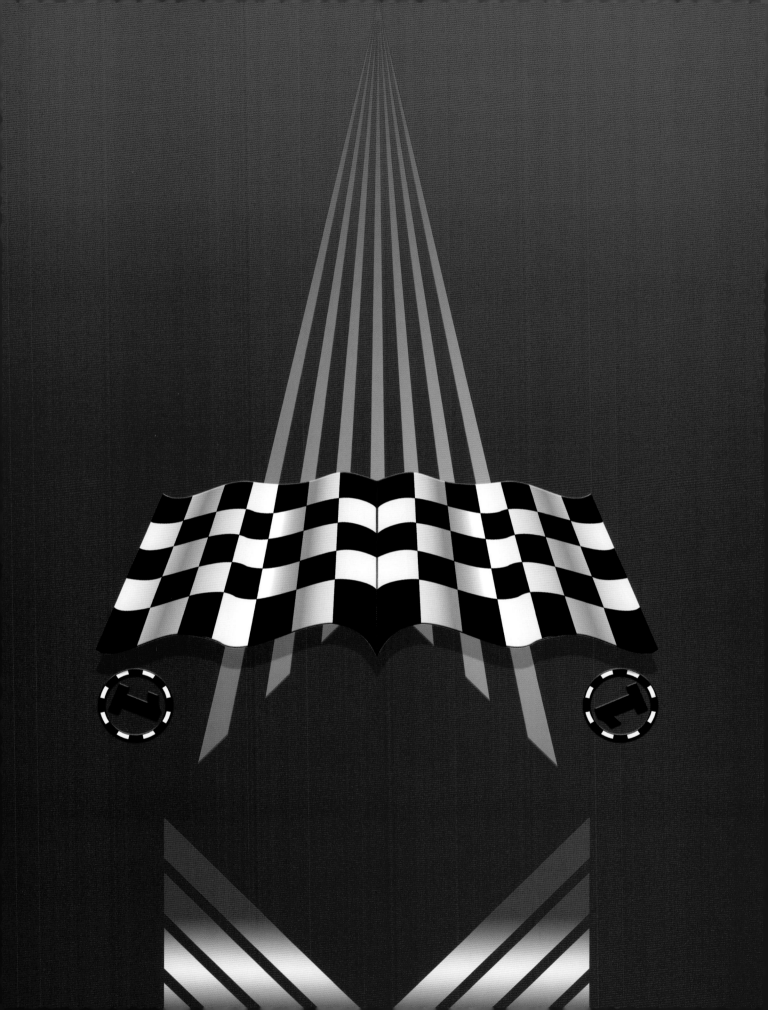

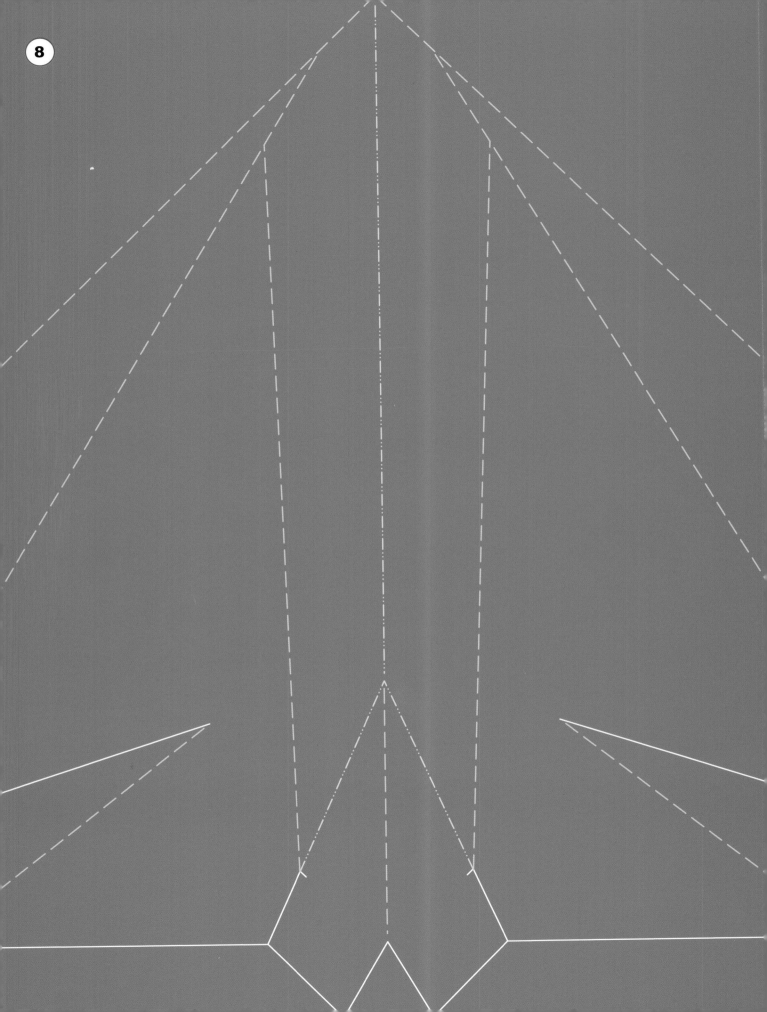

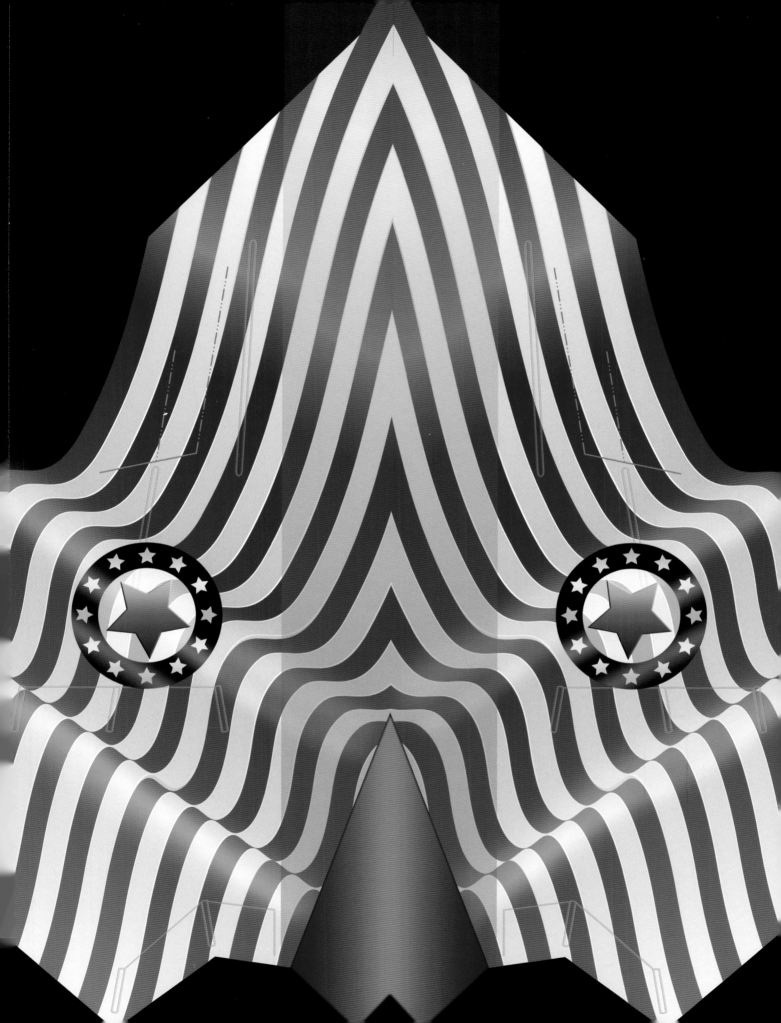

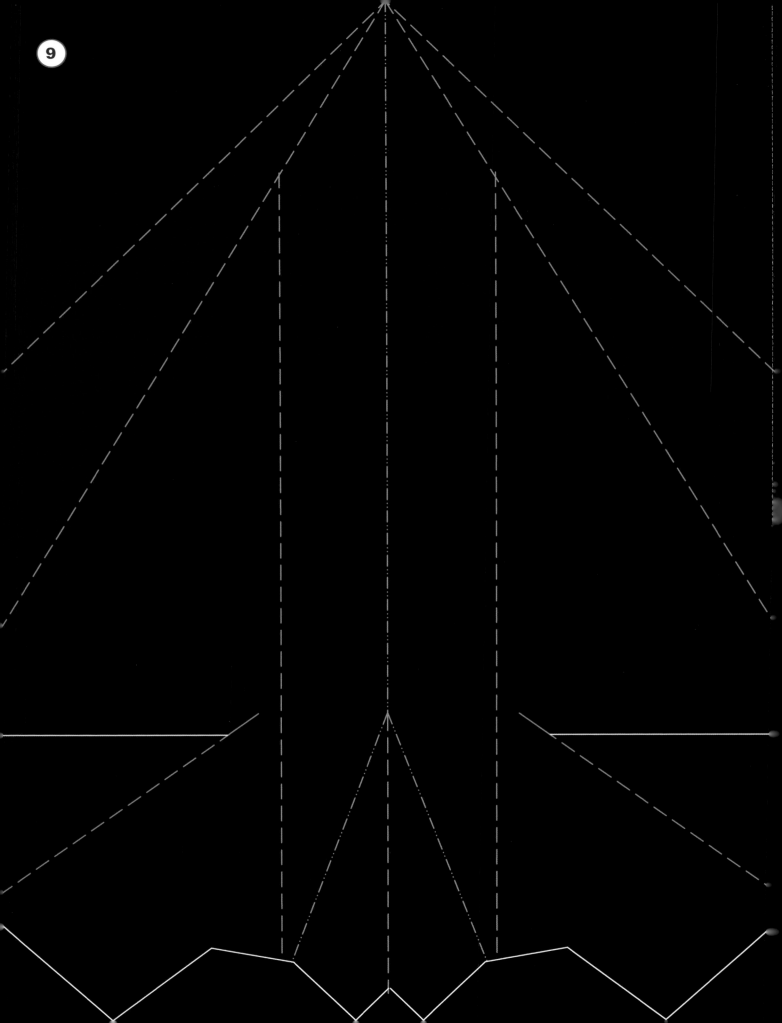

9

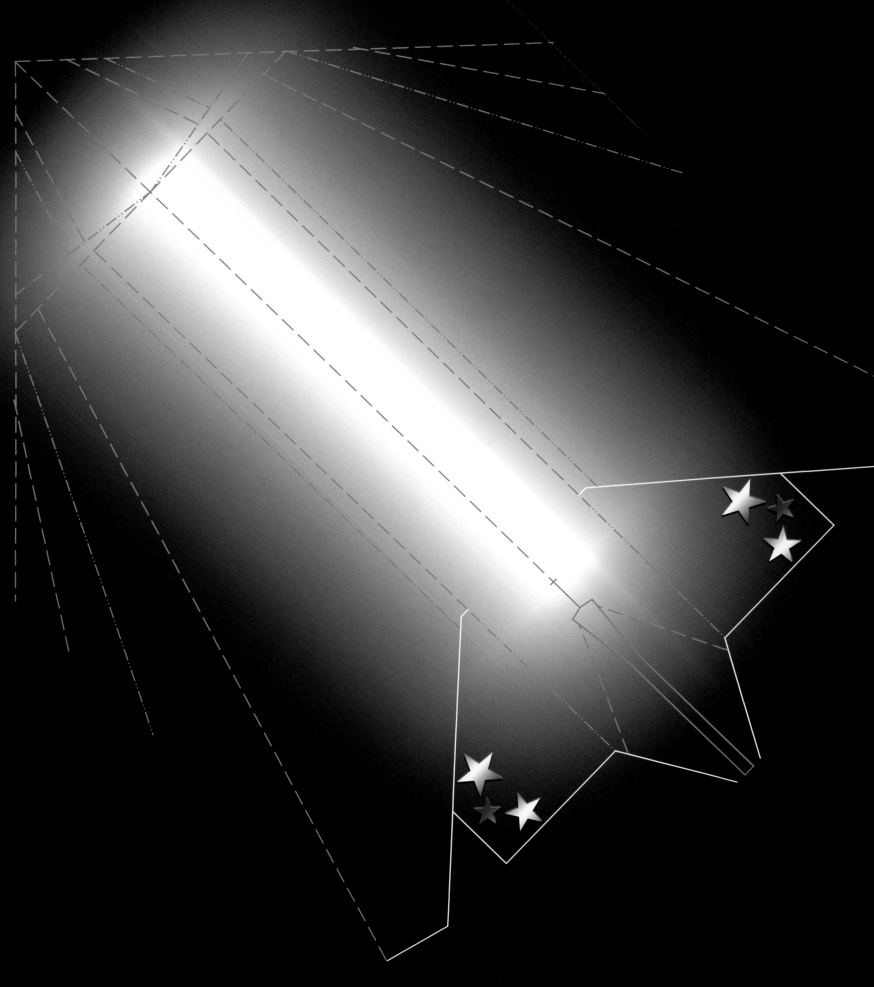

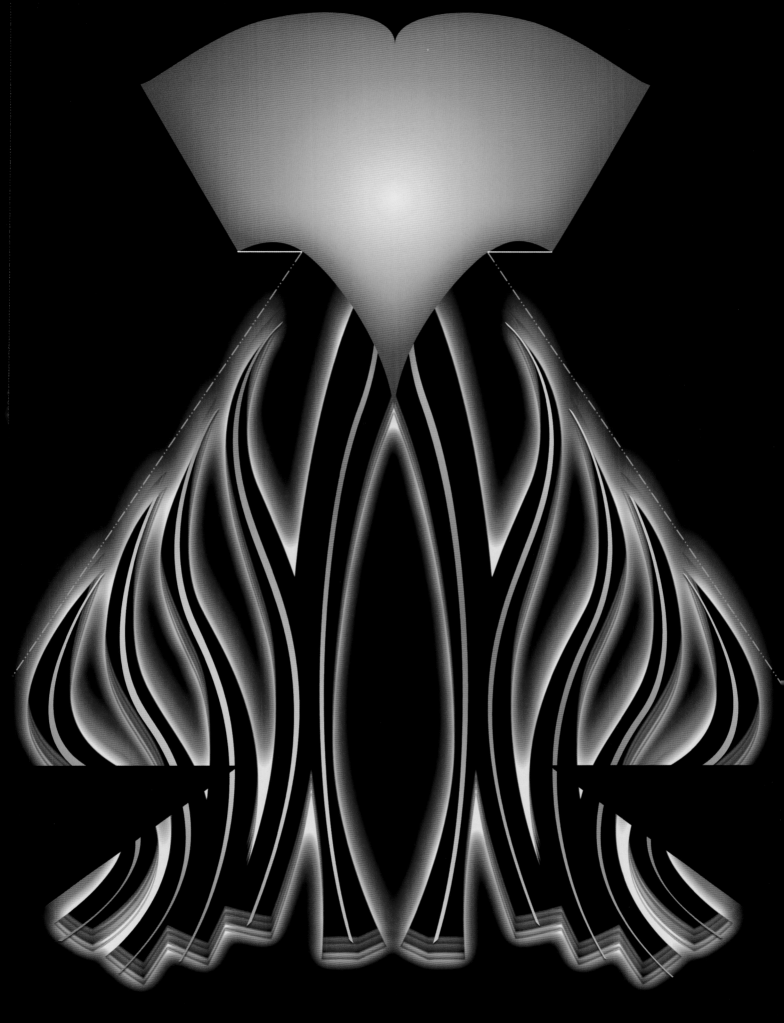

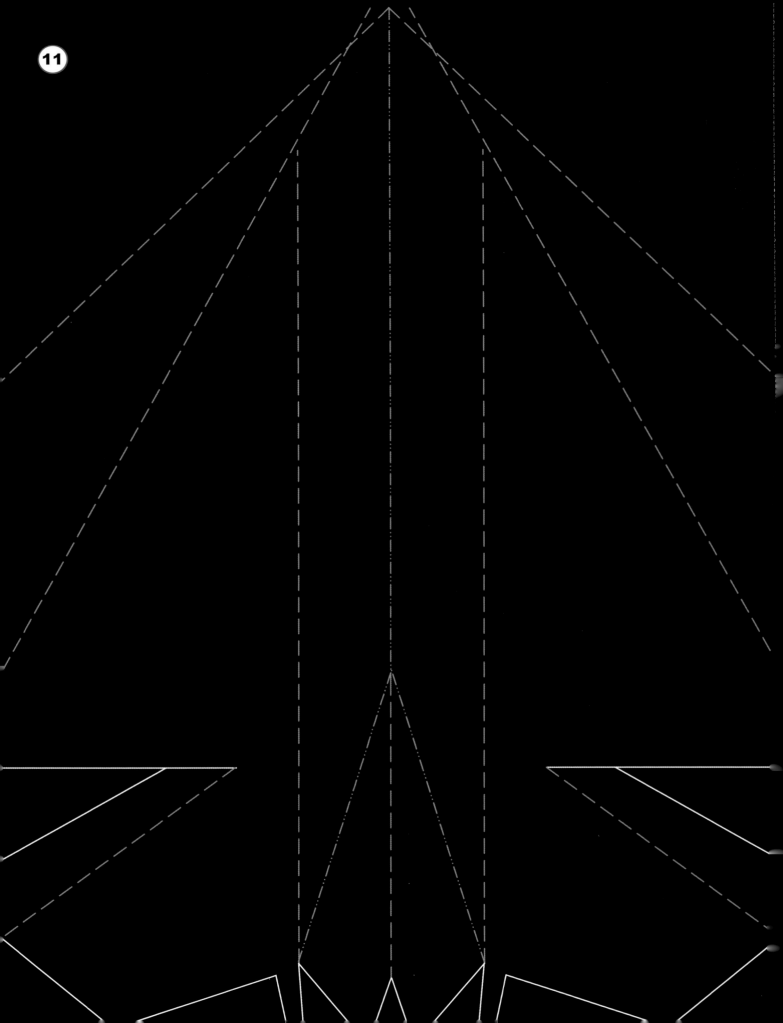

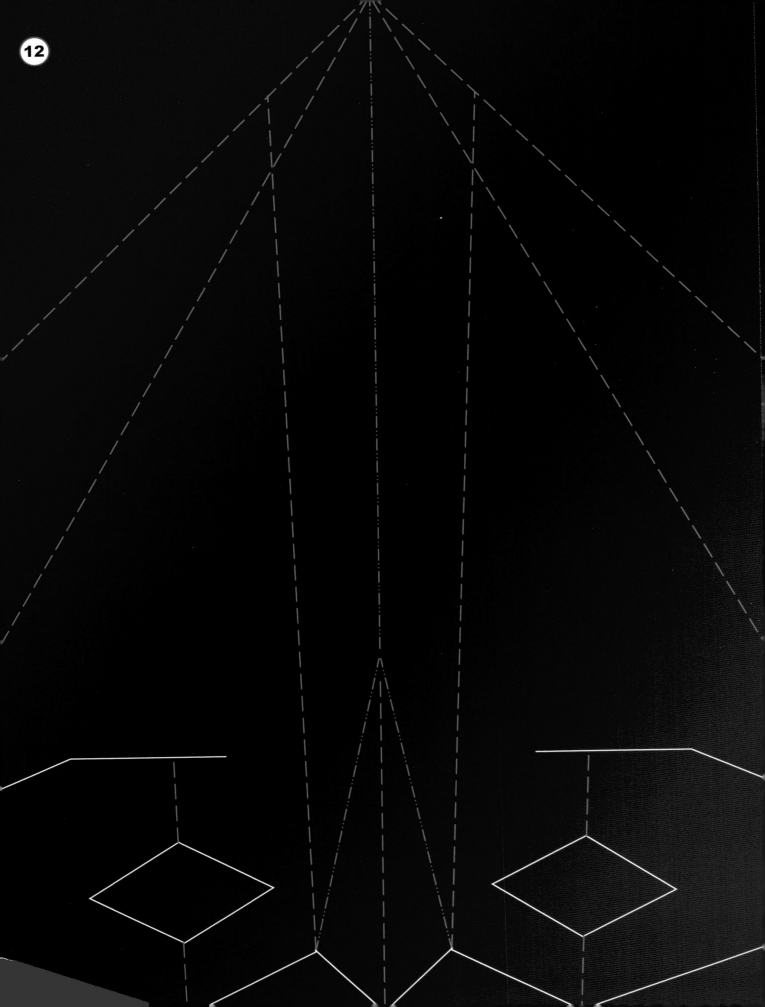

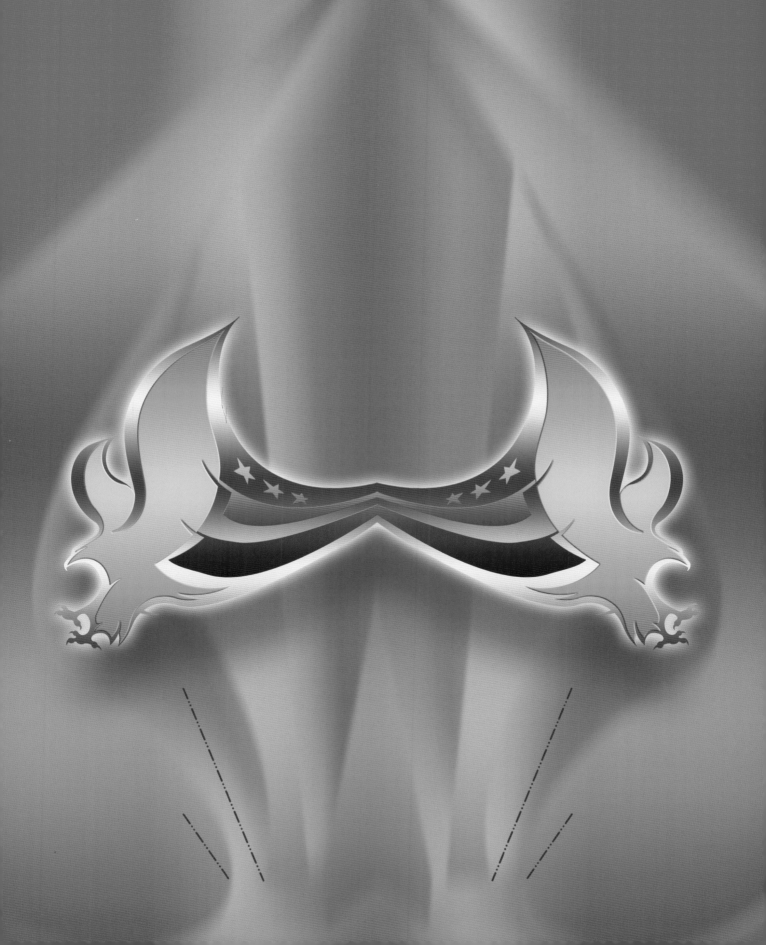

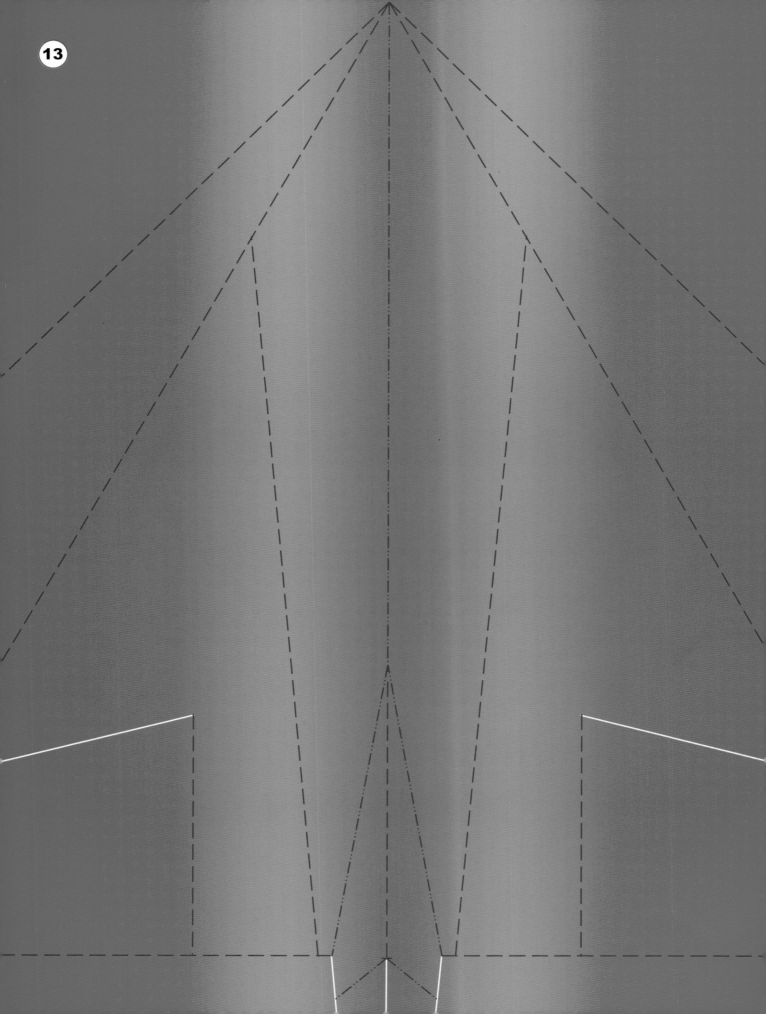

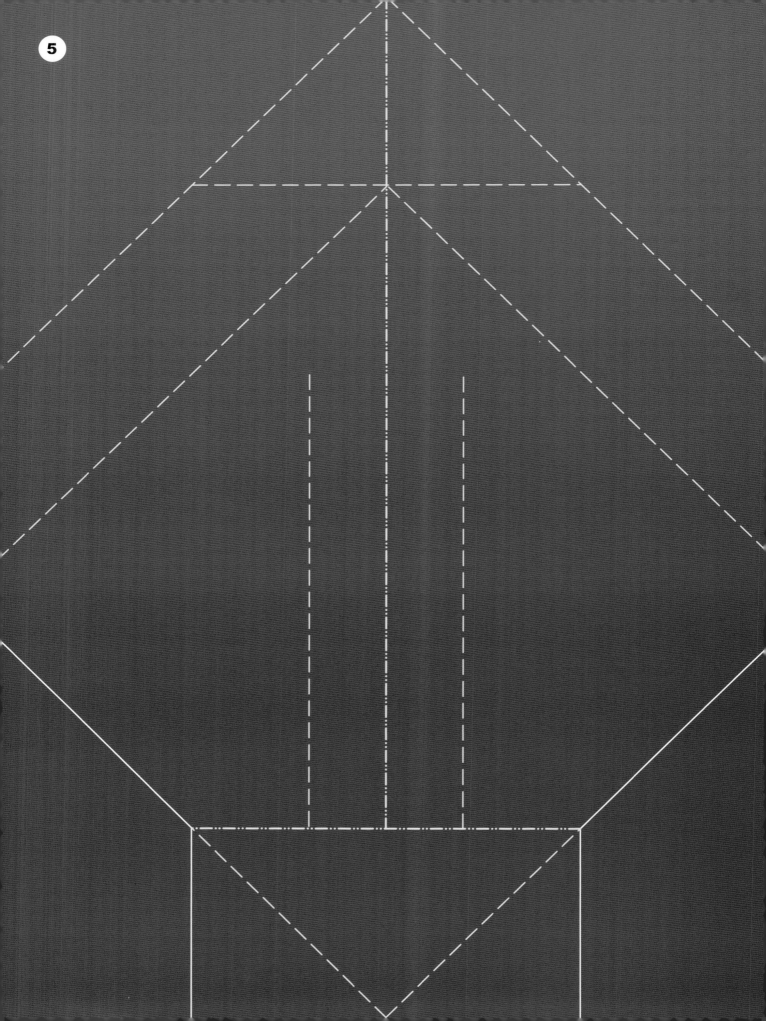

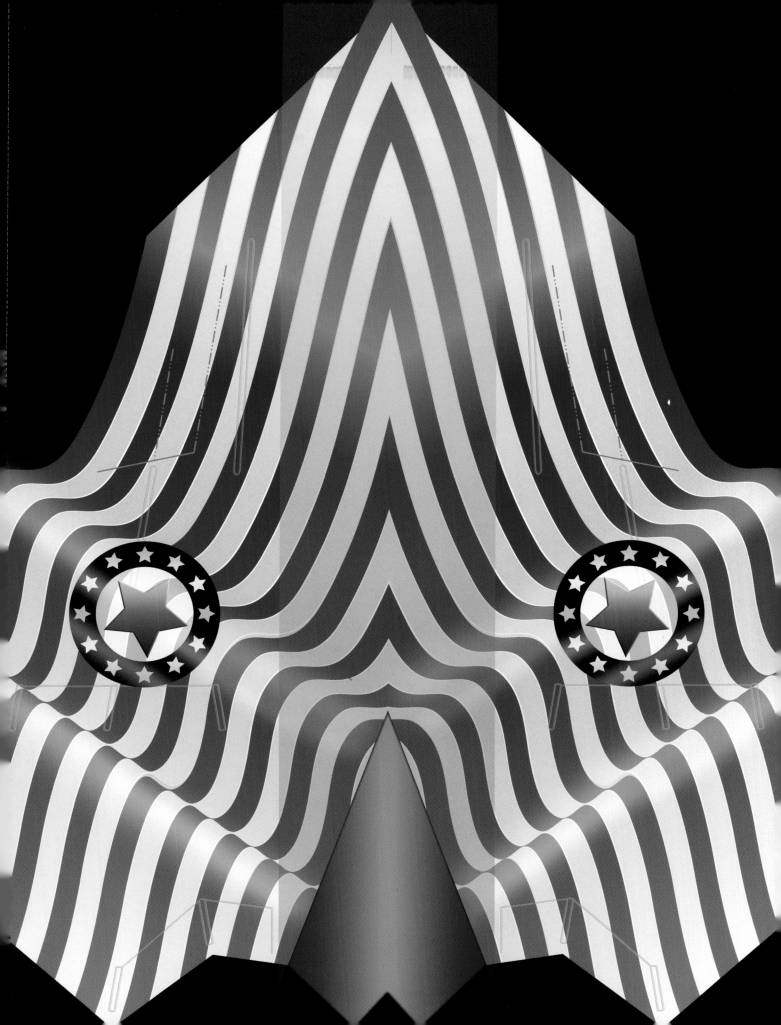

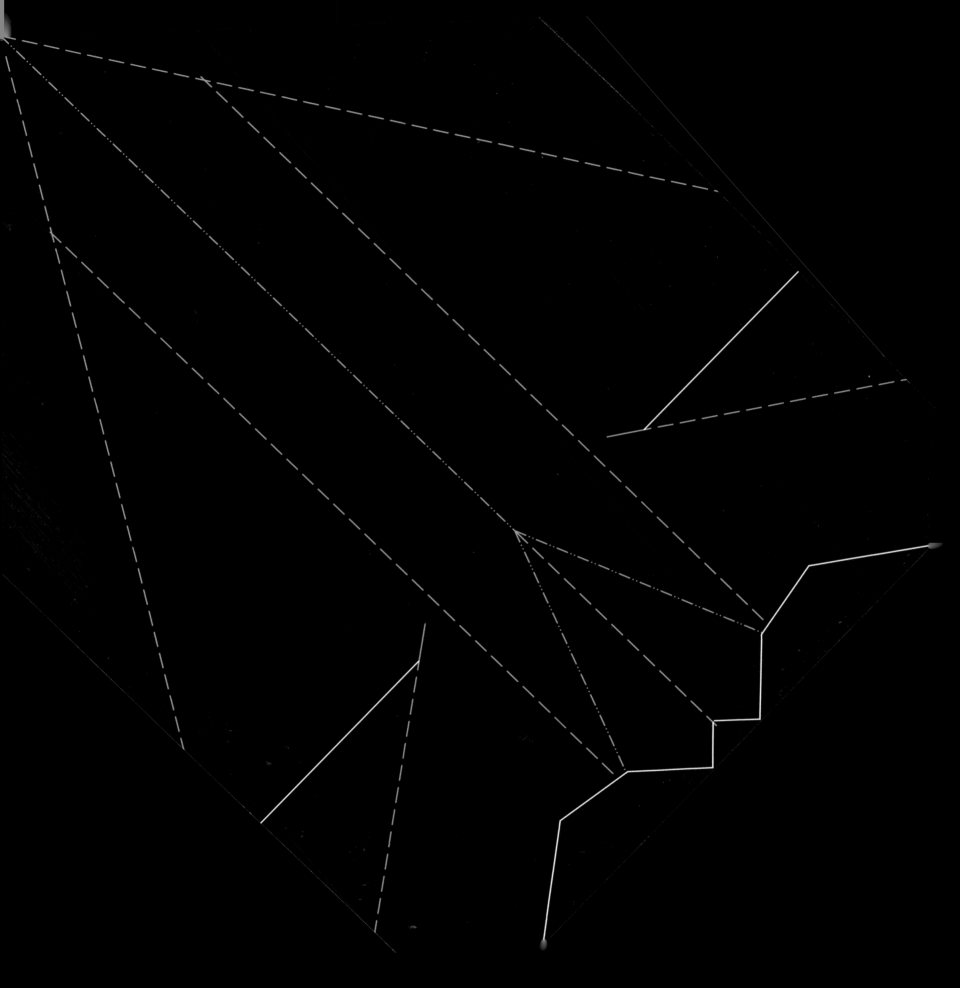

SUPERSONIC FLIERS

imagine THAT!™

Imagine That! is an imprint of Top That! Publishing plc
27101 Breakers Cove, Valencia, CA 91355
www.topthatpublishing.com

FOLDING TIPS

BEFORE YOU BEGIN ANY OF THE PROJECTS IN THIS SECTION, HERE ARE SOME HELPFUL TIPS THAT WILL MAKE YOUR FOLDING EASIER:

- ■ *Before you start folding, make sure your paper is the correct shape.*

- ■ *Fold on a flat surface, like a table or a book.*

- ■ *Make your folds and cuts neat and accurate.*

- ■ *Crease your folds into place by running your thumbnail along them.*

- ■ *Carefully score along the marked lines using safety scissors and a ruler. This will make folding easier, especially as the lines become obscured toward the end of the model-making.*

SYMBOLS AND BASIC FOLDING PROCEDURES

These symbols show the direction in which paper should be folded. Although you'll not need all these folds for the planes in this book, you can use them to create your own planes.

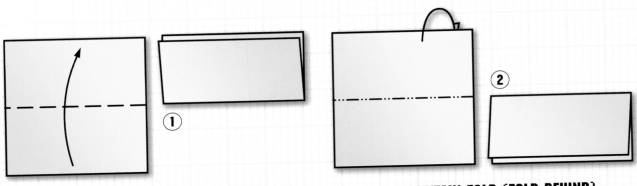

1. VALLEY FOLD (FOLD IN FRONT)   **2. MOUNTAIN FOLD (FOLD BEHIND)**

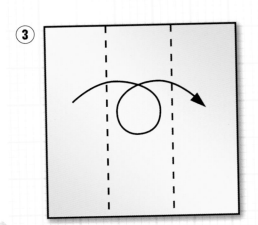

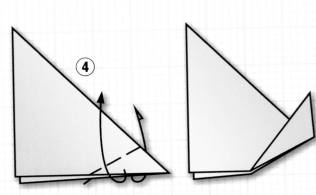

3. FOLD OVER AND OVER   **4. OUTSIDE REVERSE FOLD**

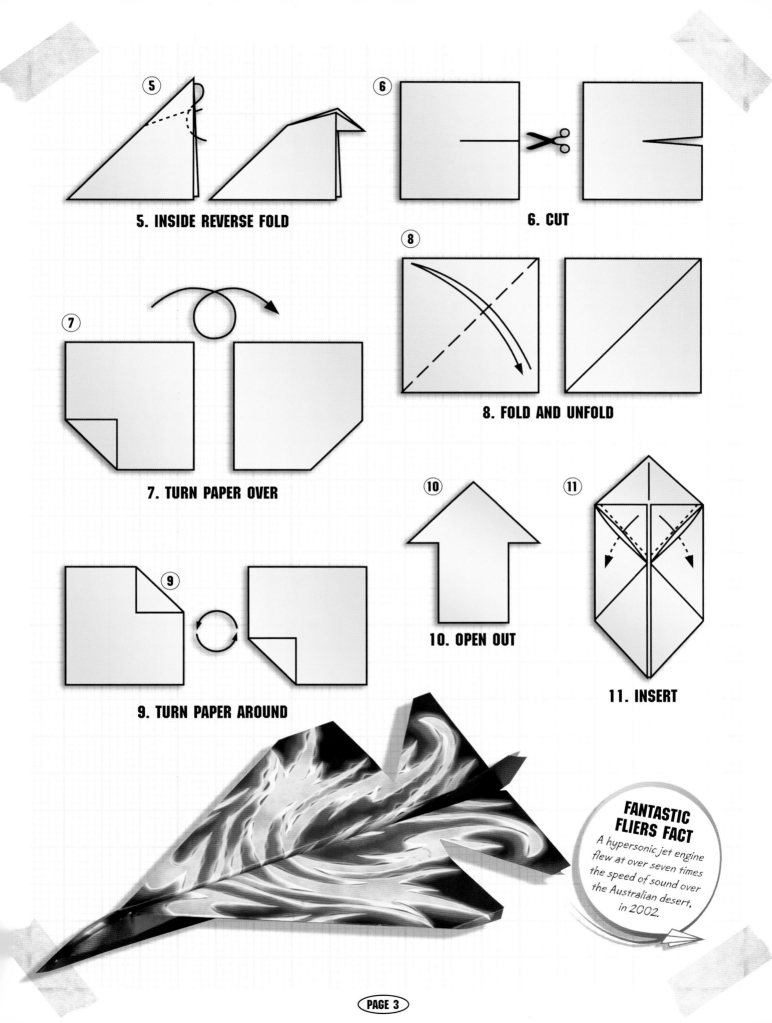

5. INSIDE REVERSE FOLD

6. CUT

7. TURN PAPER OVER

8. FOLD AND UNFOLD

9. TURN PAPER AROUND

10. OPEN OUT

11. INSERT

FANTASTIC FLIERS FACT
A hypersonic jet engine flew at over seven times the speed of sound over the Australian desert, in 2002.

B1

FOLLOW THESE EASY STEPS TO MAKE YOUR SUPERSONIC B1 JET FLY!
USE THE PRINTED PAGE NUMBERED 1 AT THE BACK OF THIS SECTION.

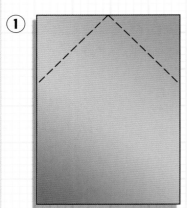 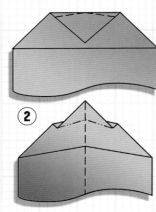 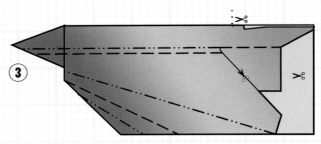

1. Hold the page pattern-side down. Fold in the top two corners using valley folds.

2. Now fold the pointed tip toward you using a valley fold along the straight dotted line. Next, make two mountain folds along the diagonal dashed lines by folding the pointed tip back on itself. Firmly fold the plane down its center, using a valley fold, ensuring that the folds in the pointed tip stay securely tucked in place.

3. Using a pair of scissors, carefully cut out the tail and wing shapes using the solid lines as a guide. Make the valley and mountain folds on both sides of the plane's body as indicated by the dotted and dashed lines. Now, make the valley and mountain folds on both wing sections in the same way (as below).

4. Next, using two more mountain folds, bend the tail into shape along the dashed lines and back up through the tail.

5. Finally, bend down the tail fins using diagonal valley folds to create your finished plane.

Holding your plane approximately 2 inches from the tip of the nose cone, pinch the underside of the wings together, and allow your jet to gently glide out of your hand.

BUCCANEER

MAKE THIS BRILLIANT BUCCANEER PLANE IN A FEW SIMPLE STAGES.
USE THE PRINTED PAGE NUMBERED 2 AT THE BACK OF THIS SECTION.

①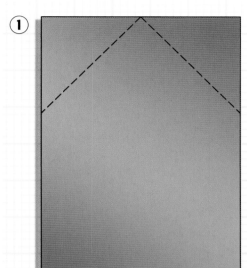

②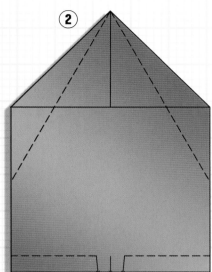

③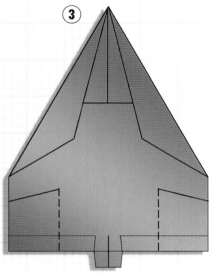

1. *Hold the page pattern-side down. Fold the two top corners toward you using valley folds along the dotted lines.*

2. *Using valley folds, fold along the diagonal dotted lines. Now, using a pair of scissors, carefully cut along the three solid lines as shown, and fold along the horizontal dotted lines on either side of the cuts.*

3. *Now cut along the diagonal solid lines to help form a wing shape. Below the cuts, make two vertical valley folds and keep these flaps firmly folded in for the remaining stages.*

④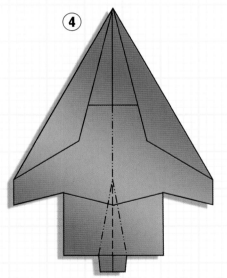

4. *Make a mountain fold along the dashed line running down the center of the plane. Form a short valley fold between the two diagonal folds at the rear of the plane.*

⑤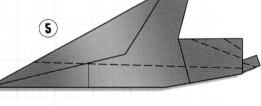

5. *Form each wing by making valley folds on either side of the plane. To complete the tail area, fold along the lines, as shown.*

Hold the plane between your thumb and forefinger, approximately 3 inches from the tip, and throw it firmly.

FANTASTIC FLIERS FACT
The W1, designed by Frank Whittle, became the first turbojet to fly in 1941.

F-16

HAVE HOURS OF FUN WITH THIS FANTASTIC F-16.
USE THE PRINTED PAGE NUMBERED 3 AT THE BACK OF THIS SECTION.

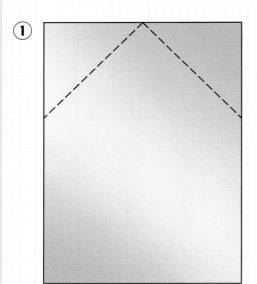

1. Hold the page pattern-side down. Fold in the top two corners using valley folds.

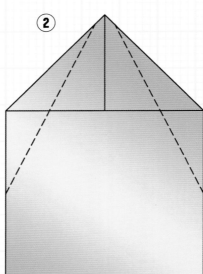

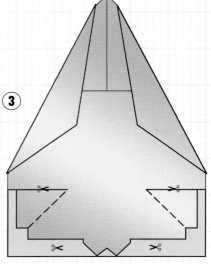

2. Make two more valley folds along the diagonal dotted lines.

4. Make a mountain fold along the dashed line running down the center of the plane. Form a short valley fold between the two diagonal mountain folds at the rear of the plane.

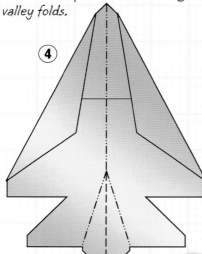

3. Using a pair of scissors, carefully cut along the solid lines to begin forming the wings and tail shape. Below the slits you have just made, make two diagonal valley folds to create the side tail fins.

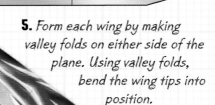

5. Form each wing by making valley folds on either side of the plane. Using valley folds, bend the wing tips into position.

FANTASTIC FLIERS FACT
The Jumbo Jet 747 began flying in 1970 and could carry nearly 500 passengers.

Hold the plane approximately 4 inches from the tip, and throw gently with the nose pointing slightly upward.

EUROPEAN TORNADO IDS

THIS EUROPEAN TORNADO IS SUPER SPEEDY AND YET SIMPLE TO MAKE!
USE THE PRINTED PAGE NUMBERED 4 AT THE BACK OF THIS SECTION.

①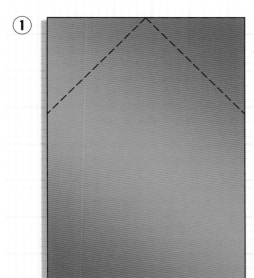

1. Hold the page pattern-side down. Using valley folds, bend in the two top corners.

②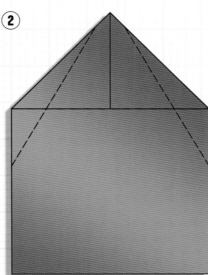

2. Make two valley folds along the diagonal dotted lines.

③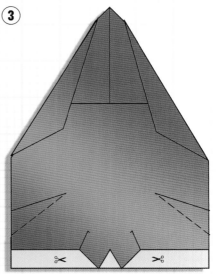

3. Using a pair of scissors, carefully cut along the solid lines to begin forming the wings and tail shape. Below the top set of slits, make two diagonal valley folds to create the side tail fins.

④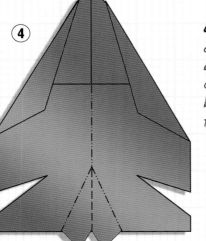

4. Make a mountain fold along the dashed line running down the center of the plane. Fold the wings over. Then form a short valley fold between the two diagonal mountain folds at the rear of the plane.

⑤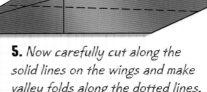

5. Now carefully cut along the solid lines on the wings and make valley folds along the dotted lines, as shown.

Throw the plane gently, holding it approximately 5 inches from the tip.

FANTASTIC FLIERS FACT
Concorde flies at around 1350 mph —twice the speed of sound.

BACKFIRE

BREAK THE SOUND BARRIER WITH THIS REALISTIC SUPERSONIC BACKFIRE!
USE THE PRINTED PAGE NUMBERED 5 AT THE BACK OF THIS SECTION.

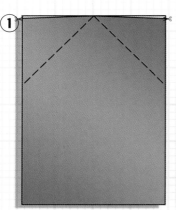

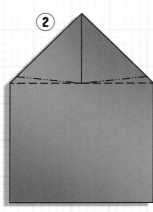

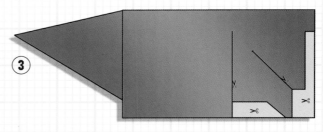

1. Hold the page pattern-side down. Fold in the top two corners using valley folds

2. Now fold the triangular tip toward you, using a valley fold, along the straight dotted line. Next, make two mountain folds along the diagonal dashed lines by folding the triangular tip back on itself.

3. Firmly fold the plane down its center, using a valley fold, ensuring that the folds in the pointed tip stay securely tucked in place. Using a pair of scissors, carefully cut out the tail and wing shapes using the solid lines as a guide.

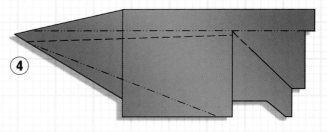

4. Now, make the valley and mountain folds on both sides of the plane's body as indicated by the dotted and dashed lines.

5. Tuck the tail up through the slit at the rear of the plane using a series of mountain folds, as shown.

6. Bend the tail fins into position using mountain folds.

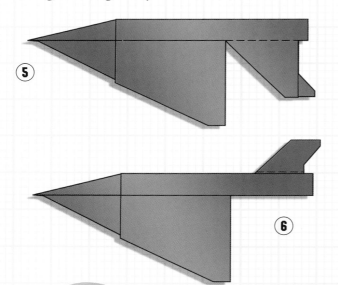

FANTASTIC FLIERS FACT
The outside temperature on the tip of Concorde's nose can heat up to 260° F.

Holding your plane approximately 3 inches from the tip of the nose, pinch the underside of the wings together, and allow the jet to gently glide out of your hand.

CONCORDE

TRY THIS CLASSIC CONCORDE DESIGN—IT'LL FLY LIKE A DREAM.
USE THE PRINTED PAGE NUMBERED 6 AT THE BACK OF THIS SECTION.

1. *Hold the page pattern-side down. Fold in the top two corners using valley folds.*

2. *Now fold the triangular tip toward you, using a valley fold, along the straight dotted line. Next, make two mountain folds along the diagonal dashed lines folding the triangular tip back on itself.*

3. *Firmly fold the plane down its center, using a valley fold, ensuring that the folds in the pointed tip stay securely tucked in place.*

5. *Now, make the valley and mountain folds on both sides of the plane's body as indicated by the dotted and dashed lines.*

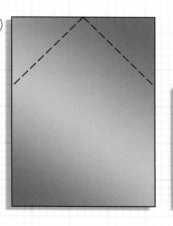

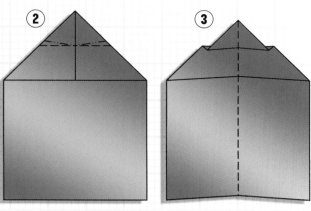

4. *Using a pair of scissors, carefully cut out the tail and wing shapes using the solid lines as a guide.*

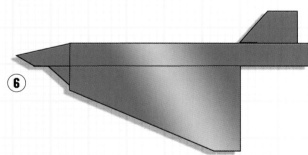

6. *Using mountain folds, tuck the tail into position through the slit at the rear of the plane, making sure that it interlocks.*

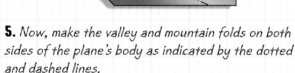

Slot your forefinger into the underside the wings, around 2 inches from the tip, and gently throw your plane.

FANTASTIC FLIERS FACT
For over 35 years, the SR-71 Blackbird has been the world's fastest combat aircraft.

STRIKEFIGHTER

MAKE THIS STUNNING STRIKEFIGHTER IN MINUTES.
USE THE PRINTED PAGE NUMBERED 7 AT THE BACK OF THIS SECTION.

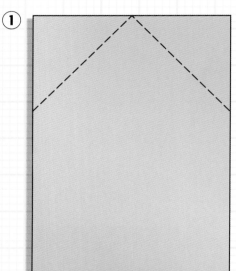

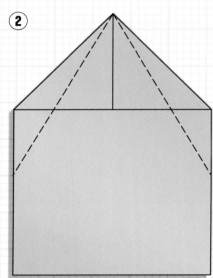

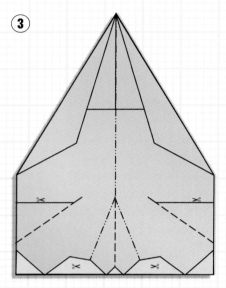

1. Hold the page pattern-side down. Using valley folds, fold in the top two corners.

2. Make two more valley folds along the two diagonal dotted lines.

3. Using scissors, cut along the solid lines around the tail and wings. Make a mountain fold along the dashed line running down the center of the plane. Form a short valley fold between the two diagonal mountain folds at the rear of the plane. Now make horizontal cuts on each rear wing and fold the flaps under each slit along the dotted lines, as shown.

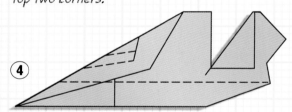

4. Make valley folds along the dotted lines on the wings as shown. Using more valley folds, form the front wings on either side of the plane.

Throw the plane gently, holding it approximately 4 inches from the tip.

F-14 TOMCAT

THIS IMPRESSIVE F-14 TOMCAT WILL TEAR THROUGH THE SKY AT TOP SPEED. USE THE PRINTED PAGE NUMBERED 8 AT THE BACK OF THIS SECTION.

①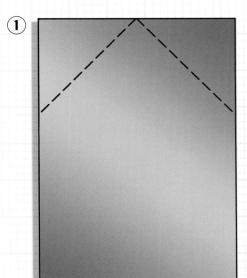

②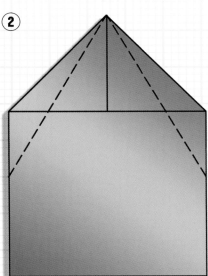

③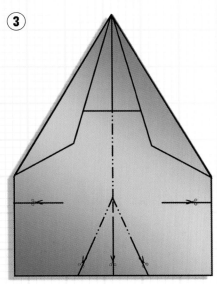

1. Hold the page pattern-side down. Fold the top corners along the dotted lines using valley folds.

2. Make two more valley folds along the diagonal dotted lines.

3. Using a pair of scissors, cut along the five solid lines, as shown. Make a mountain fold along the central line running down the plane. Make mountain folds on the lines either side of the central fold, making sure you form a short valley fold between the two diagonal mountain folds at the rear of the plane.

④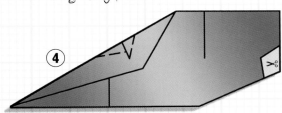

4. Next, cut around the tail area along the solid lines. Now make valley folds along the dotted lines.

5. Using diagonal valley folds, bend the flaps on the tail into place. Then, using more valley folds, form the wings on either side of the plane. Finally cut the tip off the tail and separate out.

⑤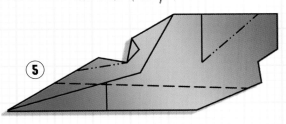

Hold the plane approximately 4 inches from the tip and throw gently.

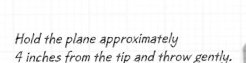

FANTASTIC FLIERS FACT
The world's highest-altitude commercial airport is at Bangda, Tibet—at 14,219 feet (4,334 meters).

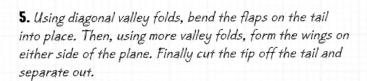

SR-71 BLACKBIRD

THIS POWERFUL PLANE HAS A DISTINCTIVE DESIGN AND THE GRACE OF A BIRD.
USE THE PRINTED PAGE NUMBERED 9 AT THE BACK OF THIS SECTION.

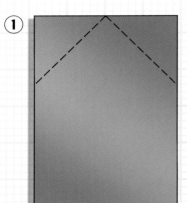 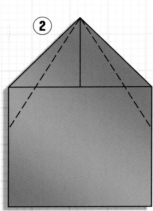 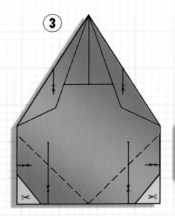 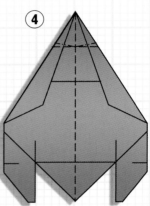

1. Hold the page pattern-side down. Fold the top corners along the dotted lines using valley folds.

2. Make two more valley folds along the diagonal dotted lines.

3. Using a pair of scissors, snip off the two bottom corners, and then cut along the six solid lines where indicated. Now use diagonal valley folds to shape the rear of the plane, as shown.

4. Now fold the triangular tip toward you, using a valley fold, along the straight dotted line. Make two mountain folds along the diagonal dotted lines folding the triangular tip back on itself. Firmly fold the plane down its center along the dotted line, ensuring that the folds in the pointed tip stay securely tucked in place.

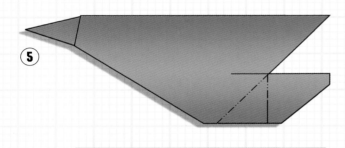

5. Slot the tail fins up through the body of the plane using the two folds shown.

6. Finally, make the remaining valley and mountain folds on both sides of the plane's body as indicated by the dotted and dashed lines.

Holding the bottom of the plane, pinch the wings together, approximately 4 inches from the tip, and gently release.

FANTASTIC FLIERS FACT
The Small Manned Aerial Radar Target, Model (SMART-1) is the world's smallest jet.

SEPECAT JAGUAR

THE SENSATIONAL SEPECAT JAGUAR IS SUPER SPEEDY AND EASY TO MAKE. USE THE PRINTED PAGE NUMBERED 10 AT THE BACK OF THIS SECTION.

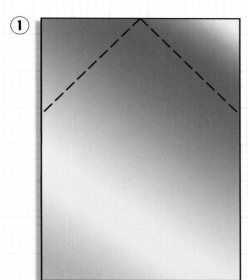

1. Hold the page pattern-side down. Using valley folds, fold the top corners along the dotted lines.

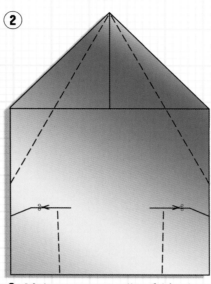

2. Make two more valley folds along the diagonal dotted lines. Using a pair of scissors, carefully cut along the solid lines. Now fold in the two flaps, along the dotted lines

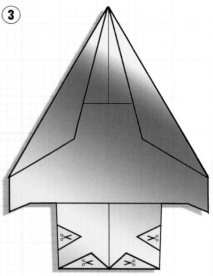

3. Using a pair of scissors, carefully cut away the four triangles to shape the tail fins.

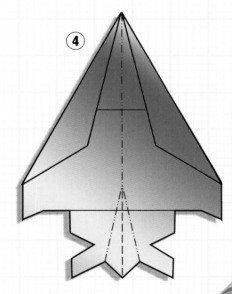

4. Fold in the tail along the vertical fold lines. Now make mountain folds along the three dashed lines running down the center of the plane. Make sure you form a short valley fold between the two diagonal mountain folds at the rear, keeping the tail pieces tucked inside as you fold.

Grip the underside of your plane, approximately 4 inches from the tip and throw.

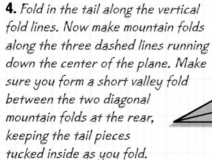

5. Next, form the wings by making the remaining valley folds on both sides of the plane's body. Finish the tail with diagonal folds.

FANTASTIC FLIERS FACT
The world's longest commercial jet airliner is the Boeing 777-300, at over 242 feet long.

MIG-25 FOXBAT

THIS M25 FOX BAT IS FULL OF CUNNING MANEUVERS—WHY NOT TAKE IT FOR A SPIN?
USE THE PRINTED PAGE NUMBERED 11 AT THE BACK OF THIS SECTION.

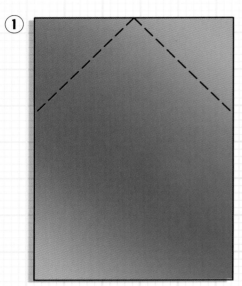

①

1. Hold the page pattern-side down. Using valley folds, fold the top corners along the dotted lines.

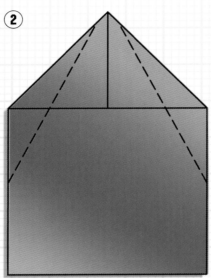

②

2. Make two more valley folds along the diagonal dotted lines.

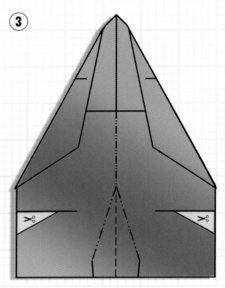

③

3. Cut along all the solid lines around the wing area as shown. Then make a mountain fold along the dashed line running down the center of the plane. Form a short valley fold between the two diagonal mountain folds at the rear.

④

4. Next, cut along the solid lines around the tail area. Form the wings and tail fins by making the remaining valley folds on both sides of the plane's body as indicated by the dotted lines.

Hold the underside of your plane, around 4 inches from the tip, and give it a firm throw.

FANTASTIC FLIERS FACT
The Gulfstream G550 is the world's most expensive jet, and costs around $45 million.

STARFIGHTER

CREATE THIS STUNNING SUPERSONIC STARFIGHTER IN A FEW EASY STEPS.
USE THE PRINTED PAGE NUMBERED 12 AT THE BACK OF THIS SECTION.

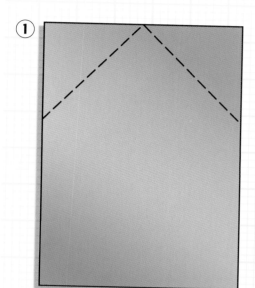

1. Hold the page pattern-side down. Fold in the top corners along the dotted lines, using valley folds.

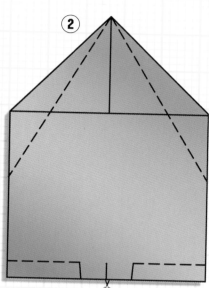

2. Cut along the three solid lines, as shown. Now make four more valley folds where indicated by dotted lines.

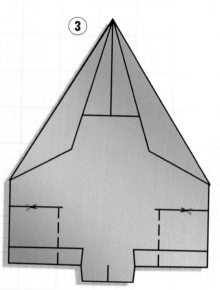

3. Make horizontal cuts on each wing and fold the flaps under each slit along the dotted lines, as shown. Keep these flaps in place for the remaining stages.

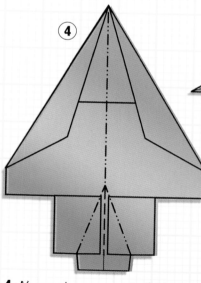

4. Now make a mountain fold along the dashed line running down the center of the plane. Form a short valley fold between the two diagonal mountain folds at the rear.

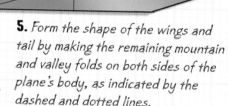

5. Form the shape of the wings and tail by making the remaining mountain and valley folds on both sides of the plane's body, as indicated by the dashed and dotted lines.

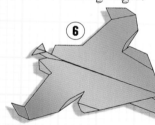

6. Finally, fold down the flaps on the tail fin.

FANTASTIC FLIERS FACT
At $50 billion, the European Fighter Aircraft is the world's most expensive fighter aircraft ever developed.

Hold the underside of the plane between thumb and forefinger approximately 4 inches from the tip and gently throw.

NORTHROP B-2 SPIRIT

THIS DESIGN IS QUITE SIMPLE TO DO, BUT VERY EFFECTIVE.
USE THE PRINTED PAGE NUMBERED 13 AT THE BACK OF THIS SECTION.

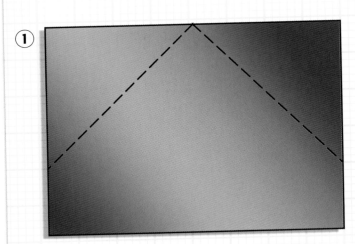

①

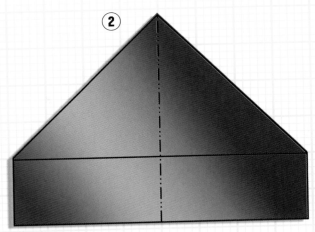

②

1. *Hold the page pattern-side down. Using valley folds, fold the two top corners towards you along the dotted lines.*

2. *Firmly fold down the center of the plane along the dashed line, using a mountain fold.*

3. *Using a pair of scissors, cut along the solid lines, as shown. Now form the shape of the wings and tail by making the remaining valley folds on both sides of the plane's body as indicated by the dotted lines.*

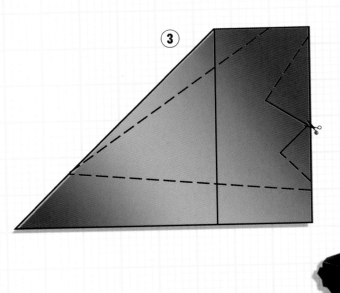

③

Hold the plane in the center of the base and release gently.

FANTASTIC FLIERS FACT
The first man to break the sound barrier was the American Chuck Yeager, in 1947.

Problems flying your plane? Try weighting down the nose with a paper clip.

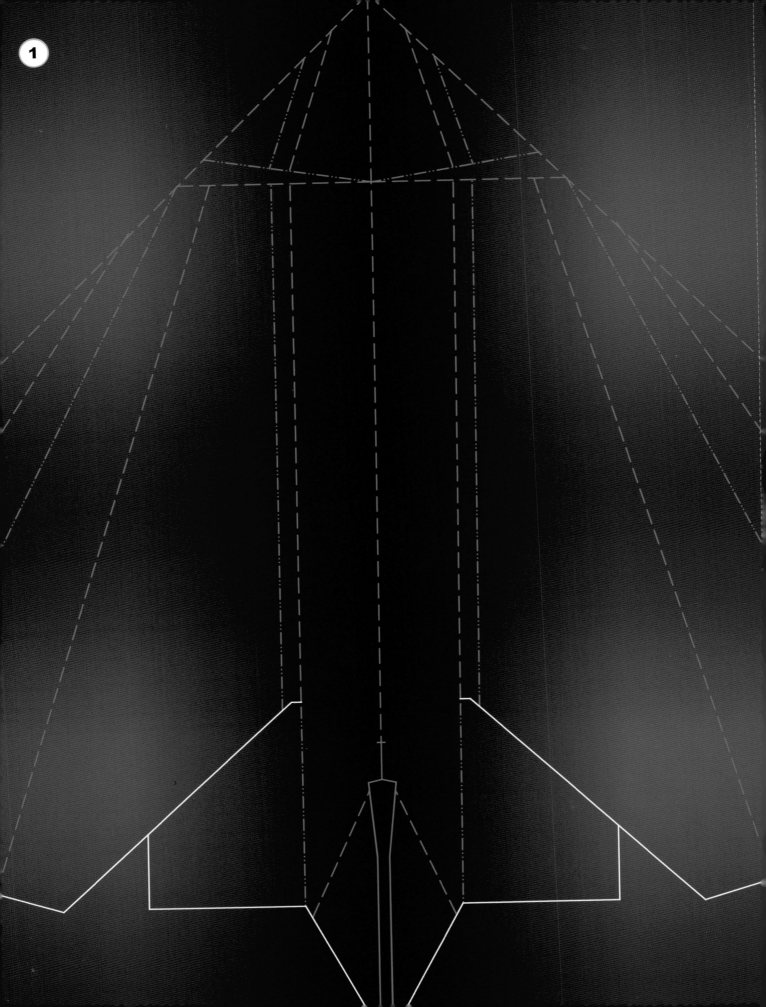

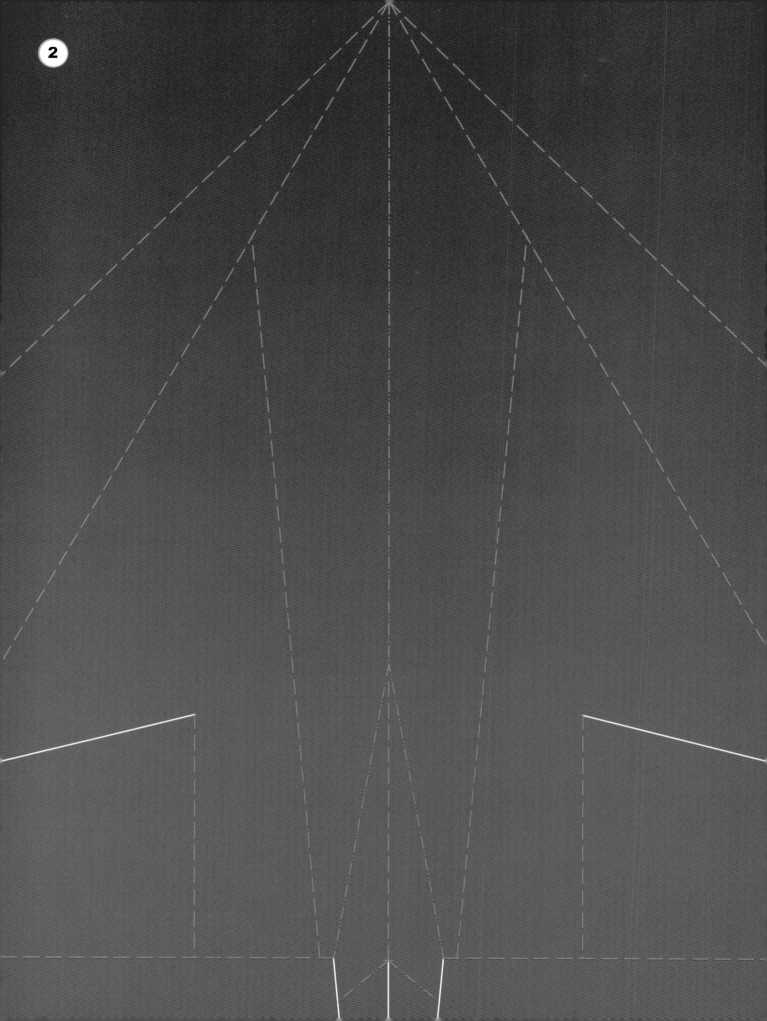

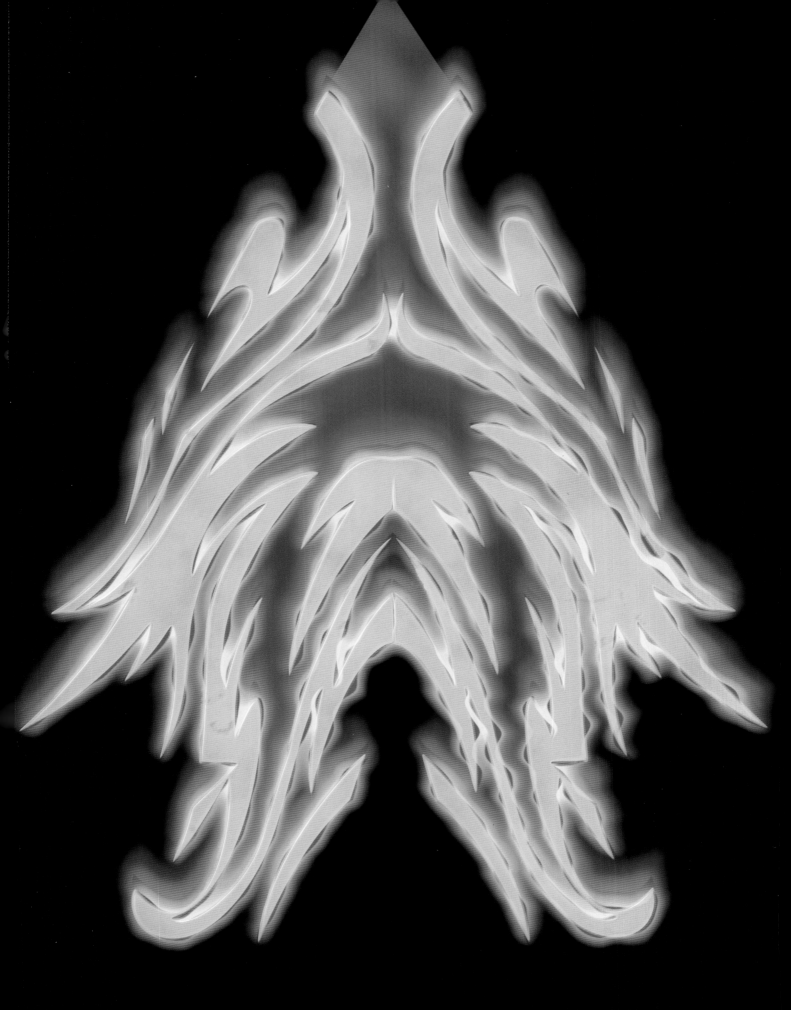

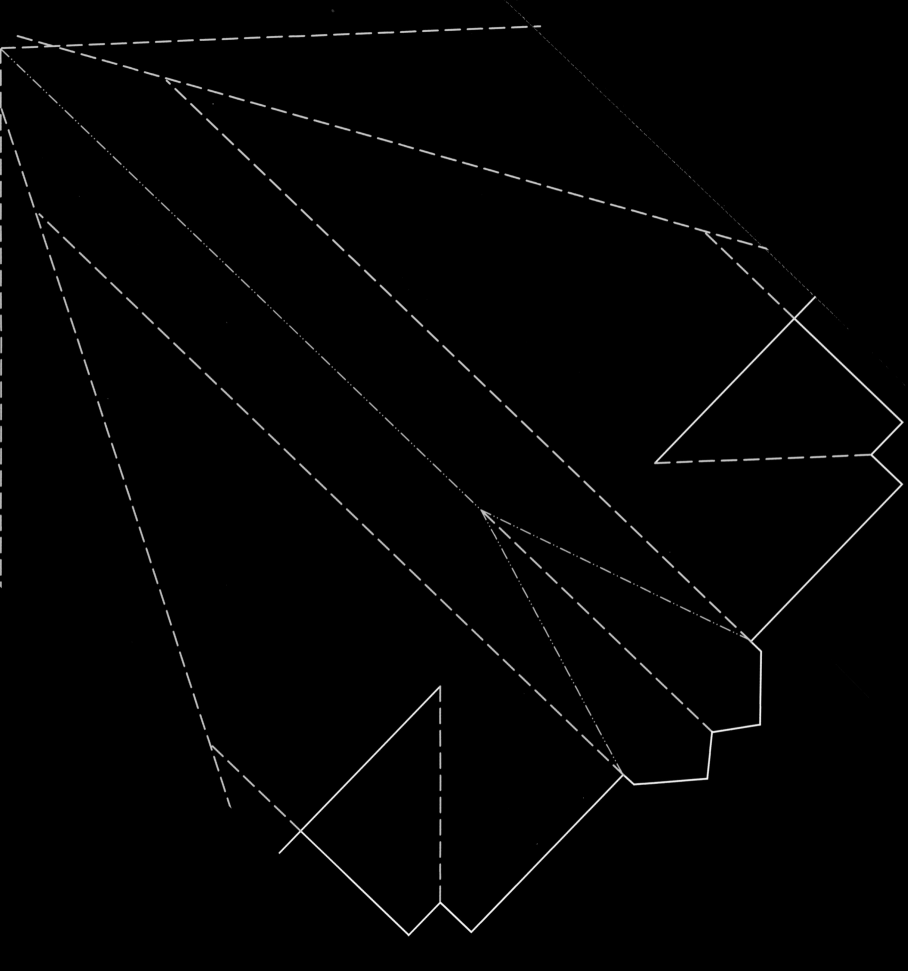

4

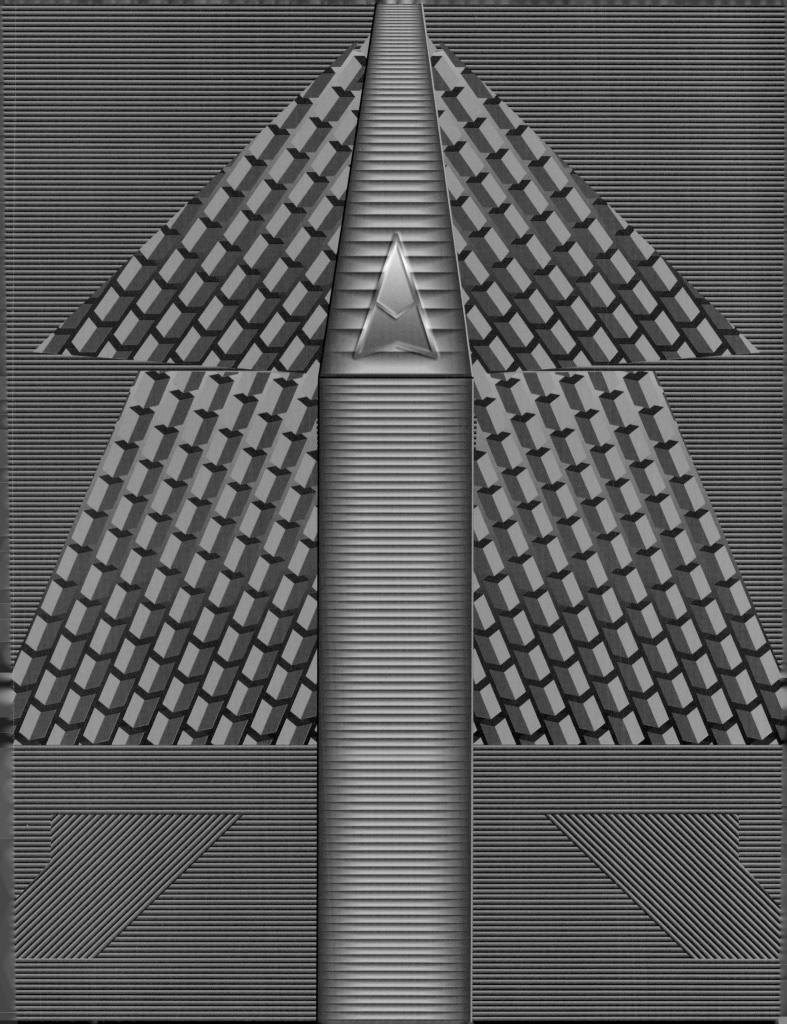

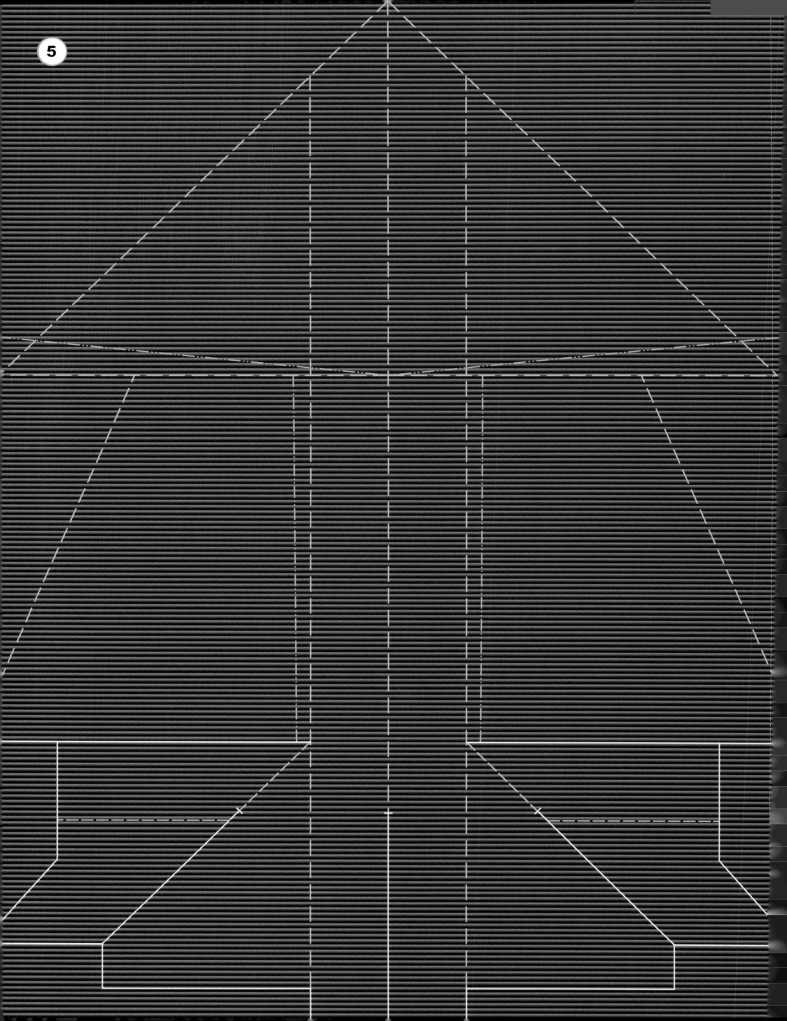

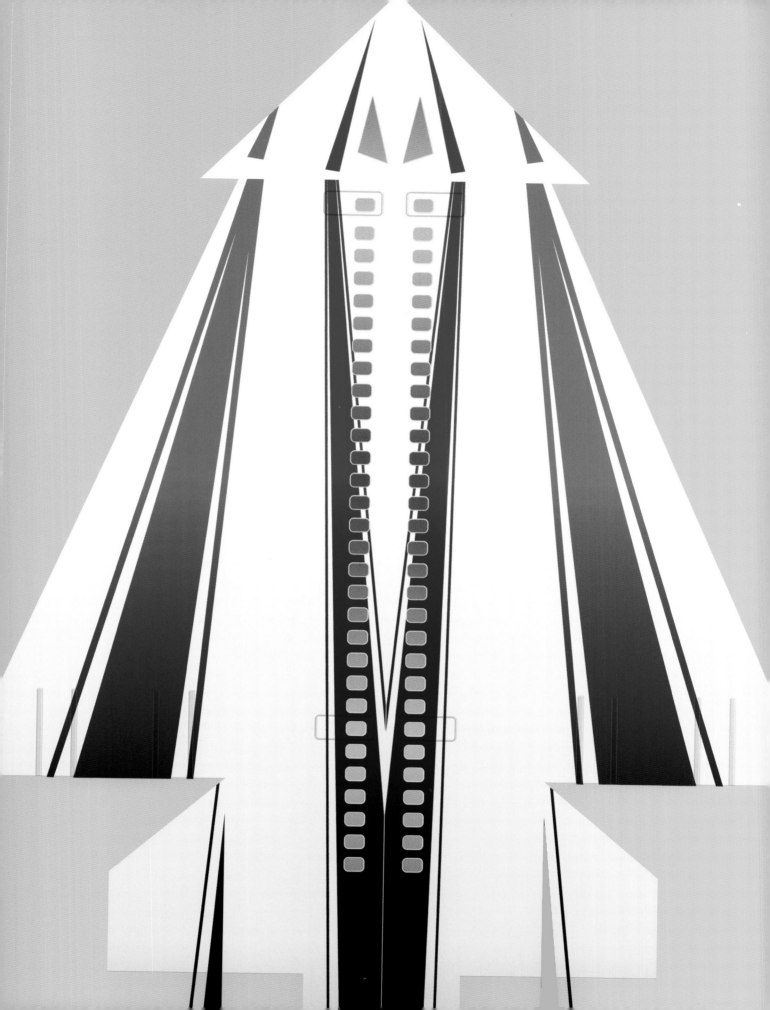

7

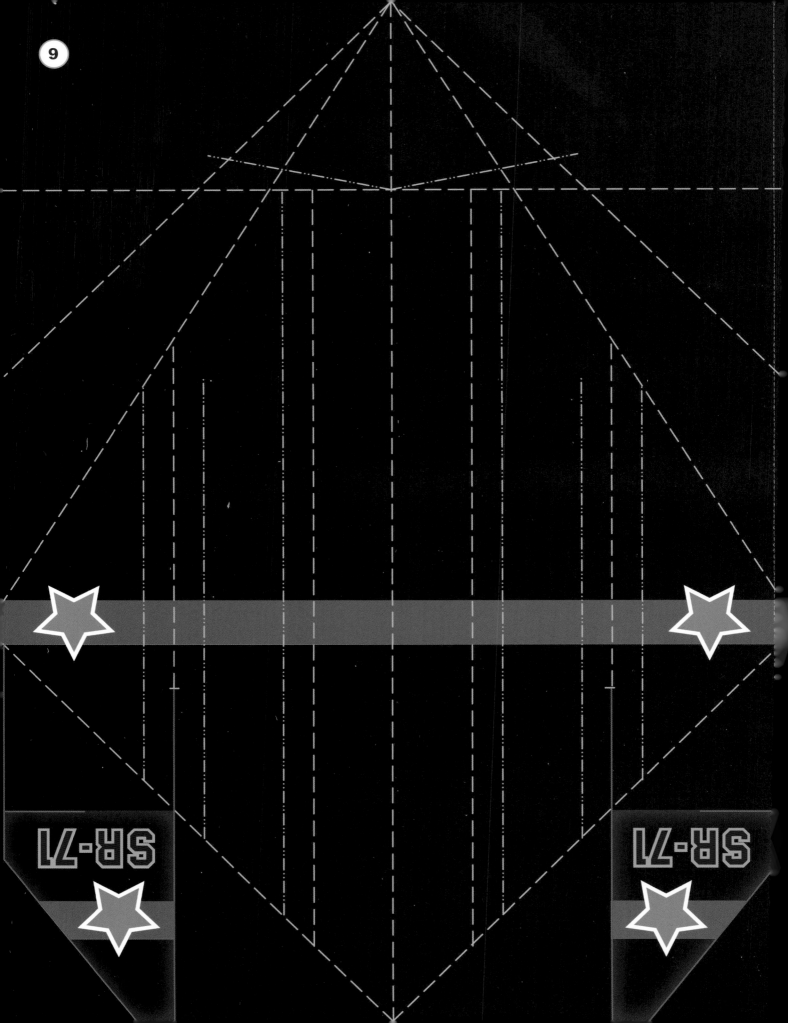

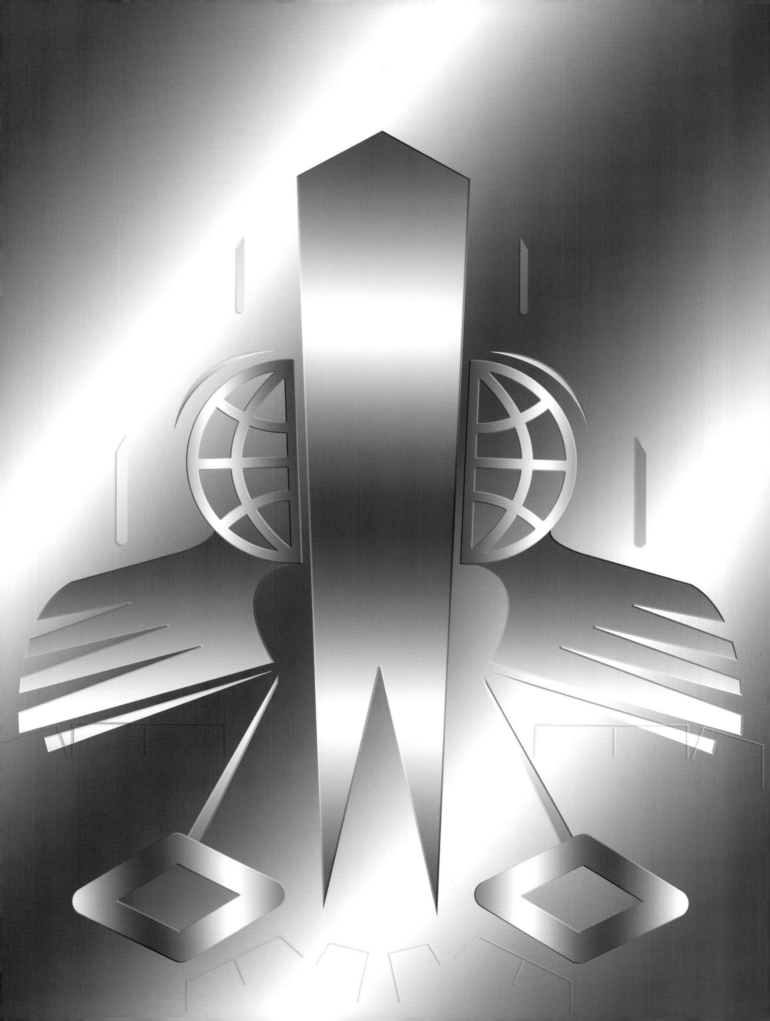

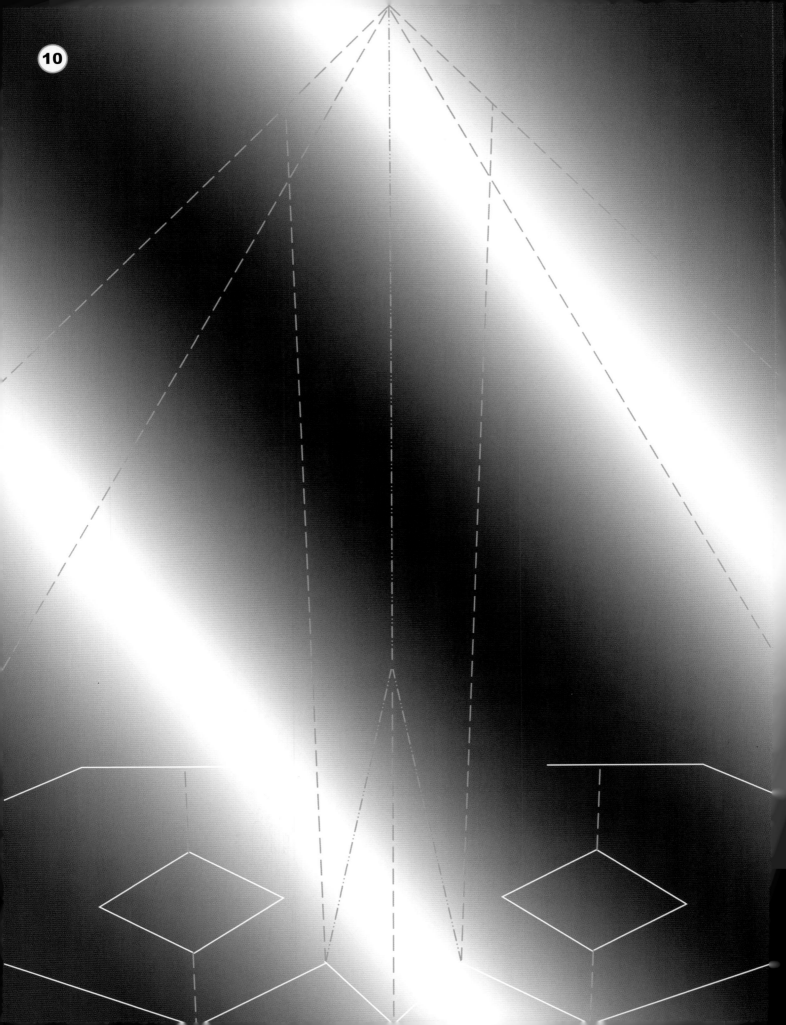

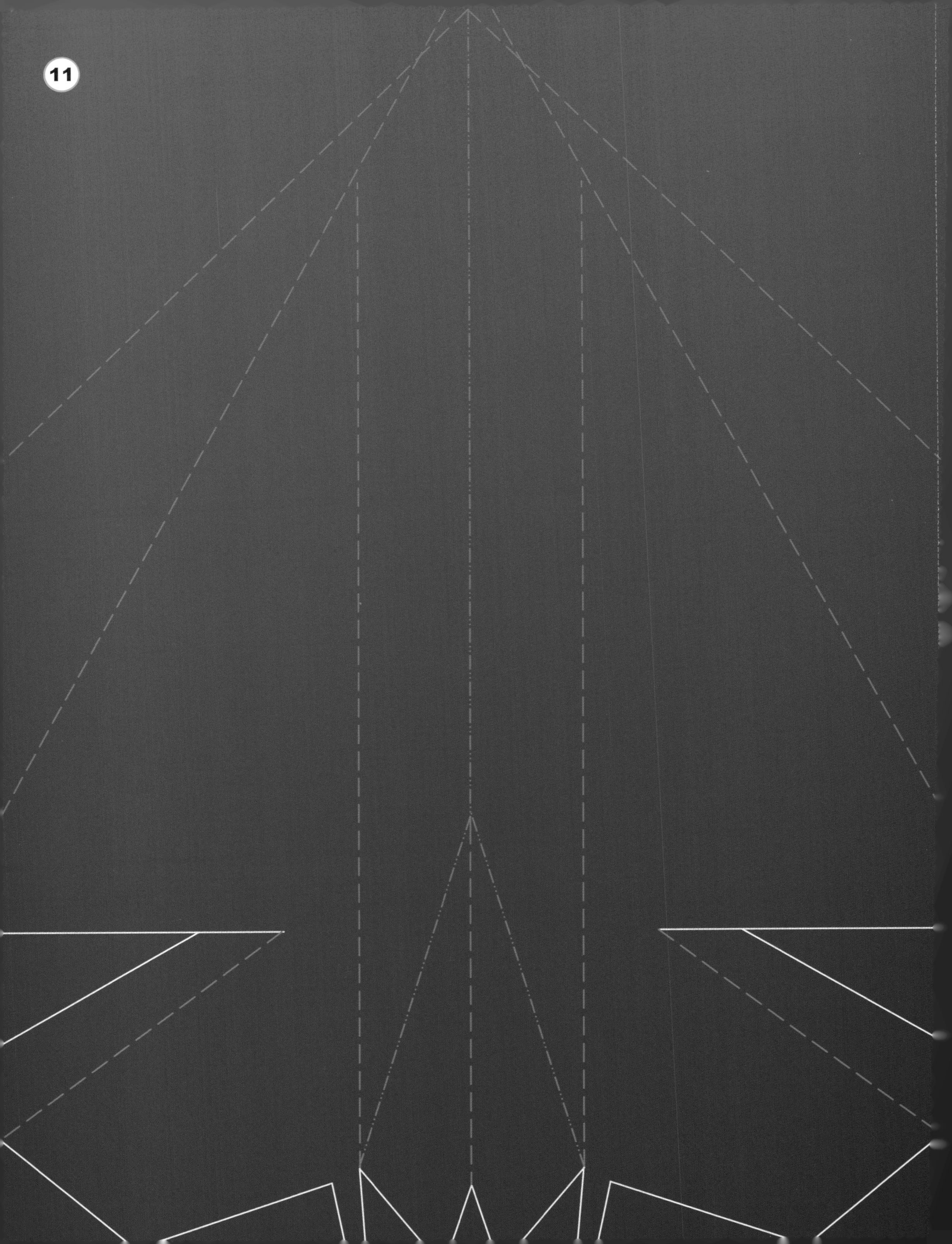
11

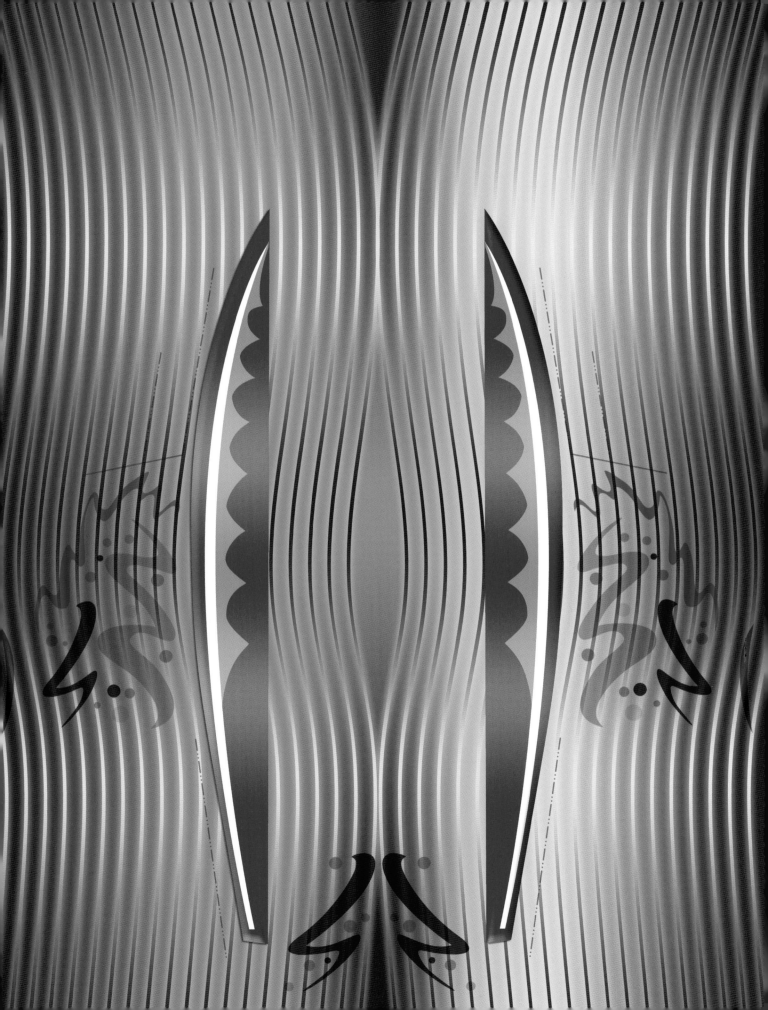

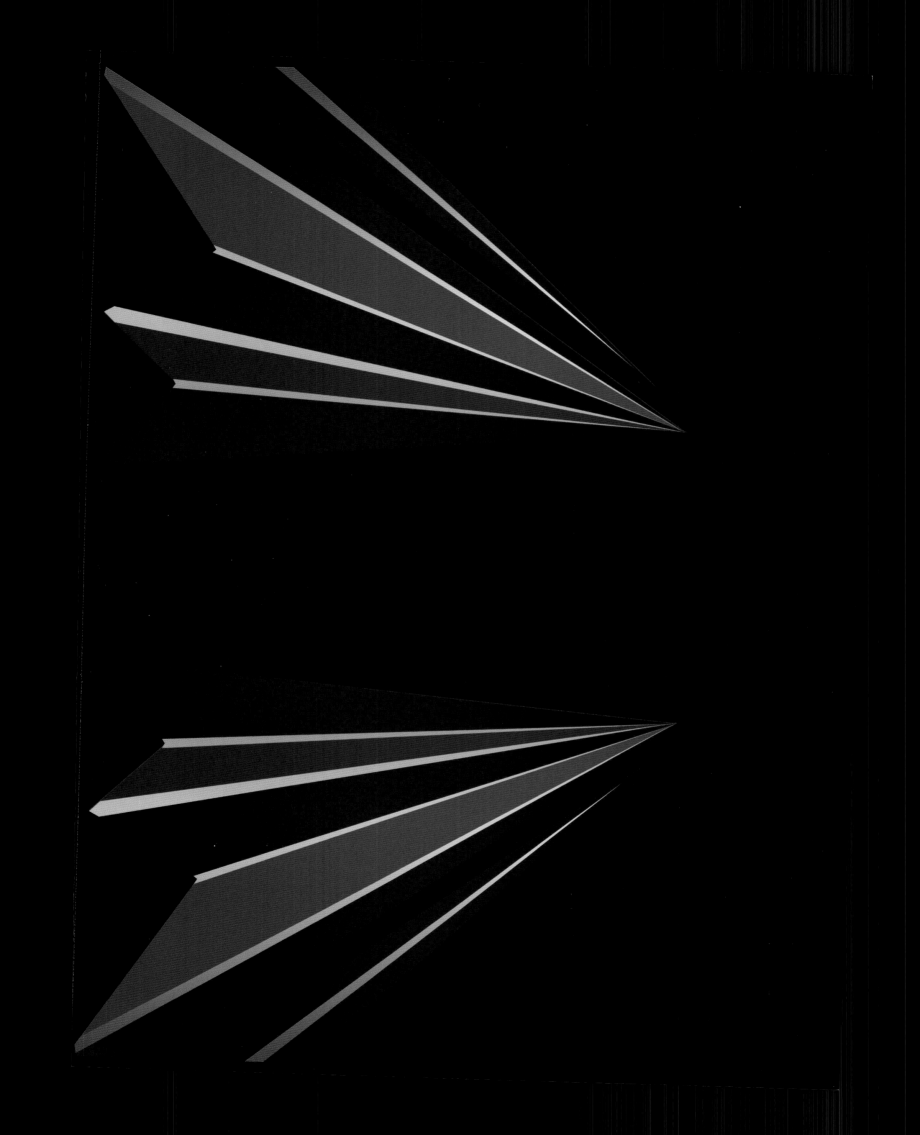

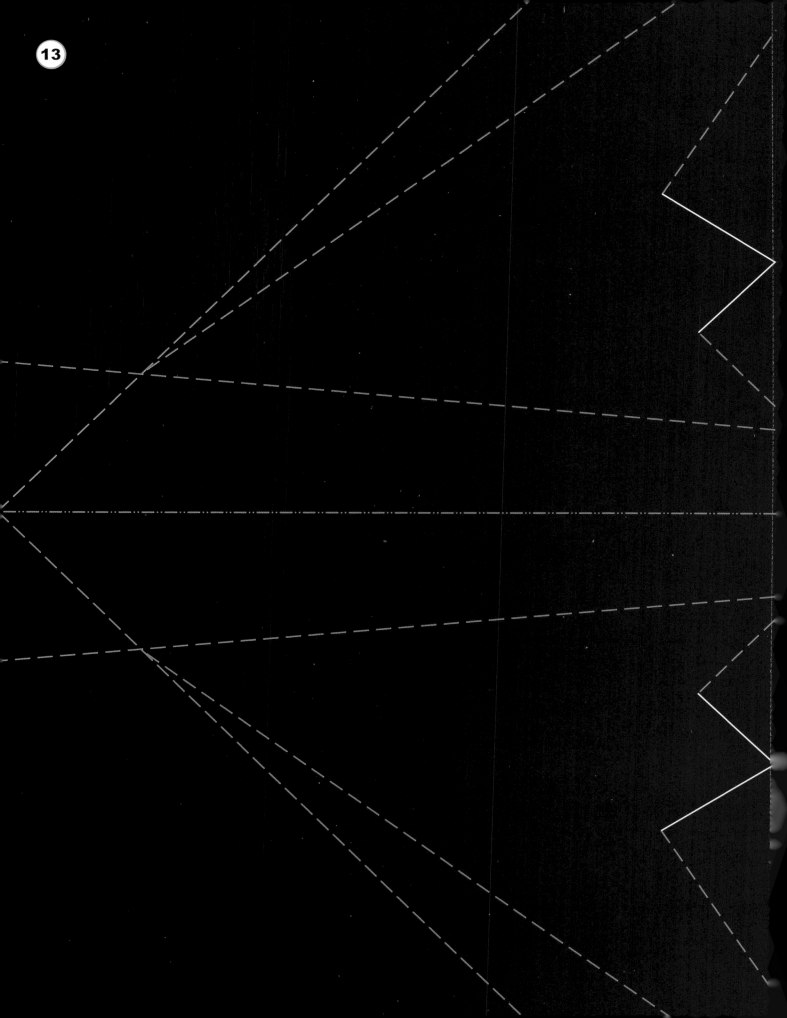

13

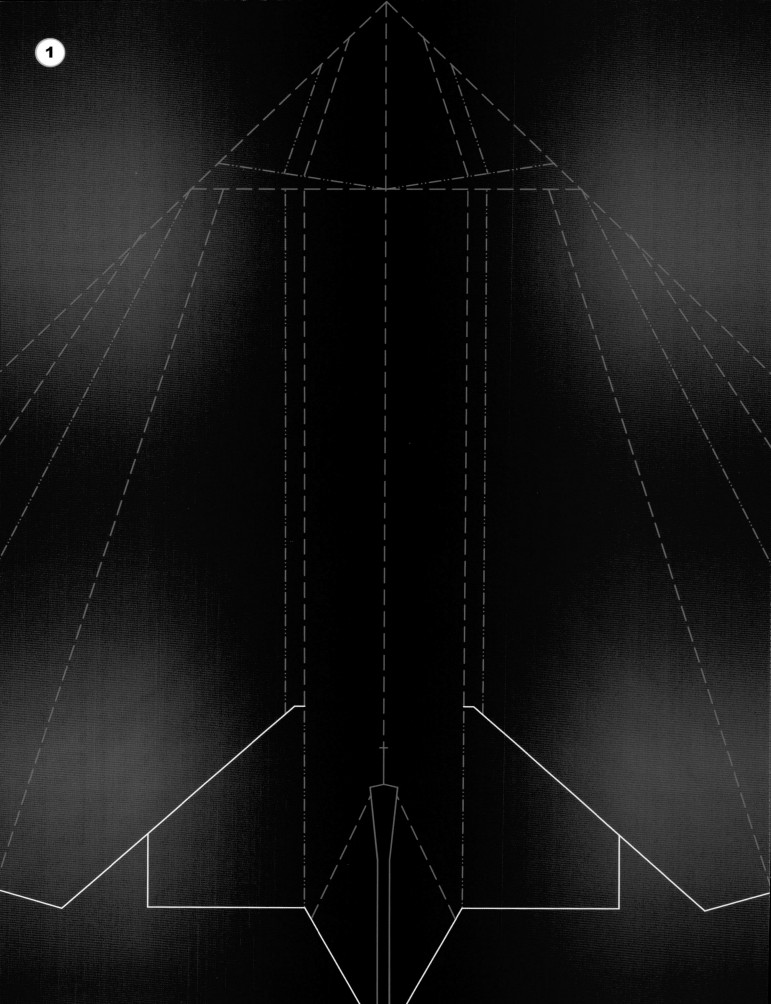

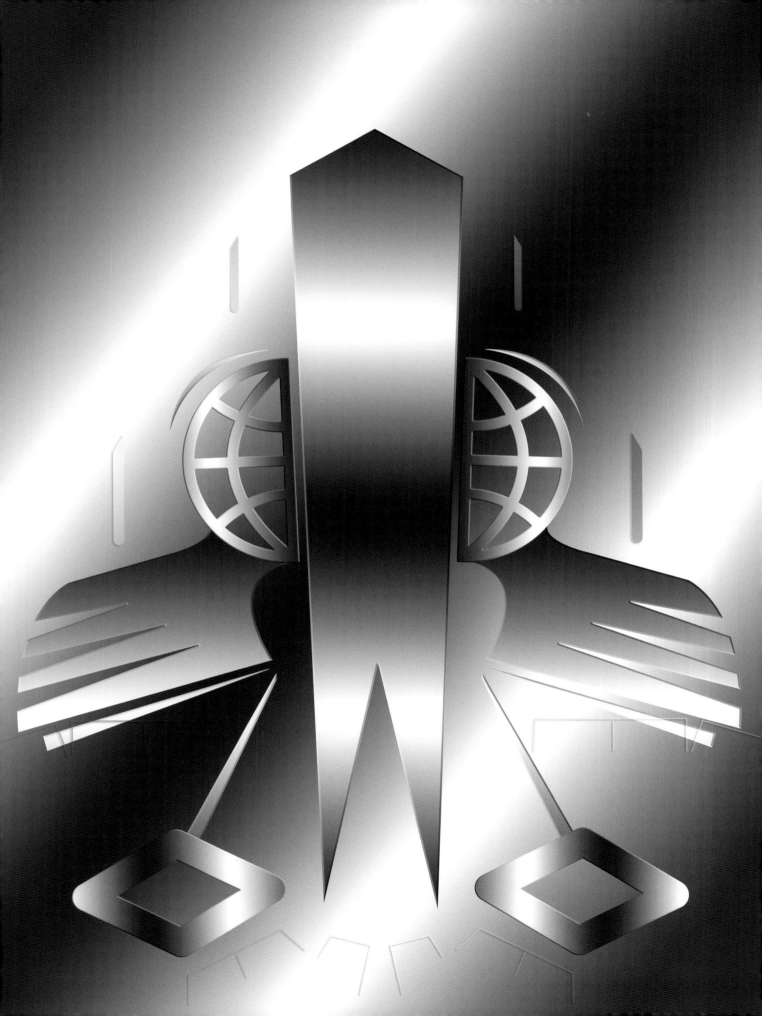

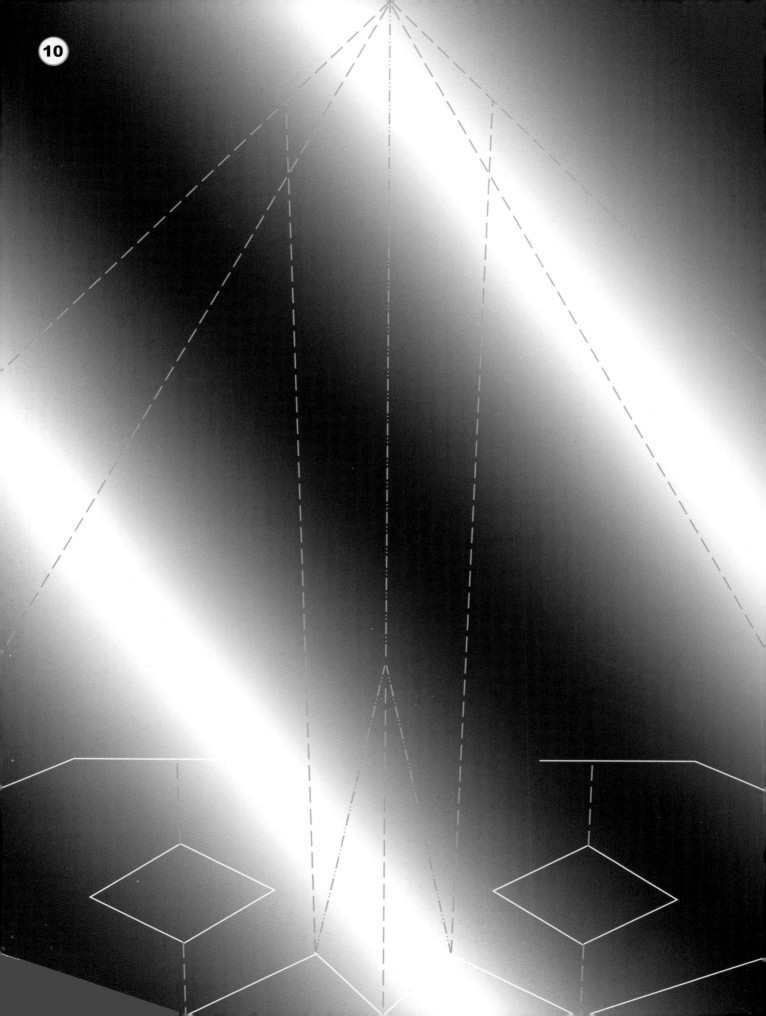

SUPER COOL FLIERS

imagine THAT!™

Imagine That! is an imprint of Top That! Publishing plc
27101 Breakers Cove, Valencia, CA 91355
www.topthatpublishing.com

FOLDING TIPS

BEFORE YOU BEGIN ANY OF THE PROJECTS IN THIS SECTION, HERE ARE SOME HELPFUL TIPS THAT WILL MAKE YOUR FOLDING EASIER:

■ *Before you start folding, make sure your paper is the correct shape.*

■ *Fold on a flat surface, like a table or a book.*

■ *Make your folds and cuts neat and accurate.*

■ *Crease your folds into place by running your thumbnail along them.*

■ *Carefully score along the marked lines using safety scissors and a ruler. This will make folding easier, especially as the lines become obscured toward the end of the model-making.*

SYMBOLS AND BASIC FOLDING PROCEDURES

These symbols show the direction in which paper should be folded. Although you'll not need all these folds for the planes in this section, you can use them to create your own planes.

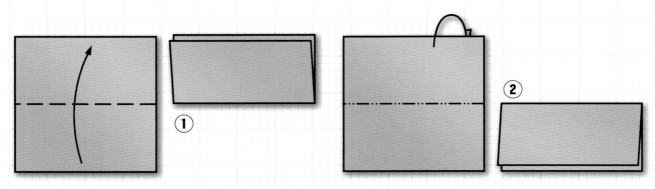

1. VALLEY FOLD (FOLD IN FRONT)

2. MOUNTAIN FOLD (FOLD BEHIND)

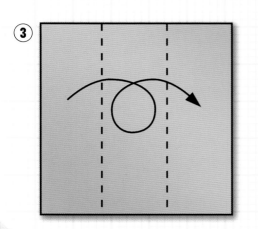

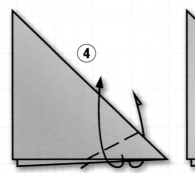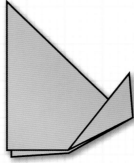

3. FOLD OVER AND OVER

4. OUTSIDE REVERSE FOLD

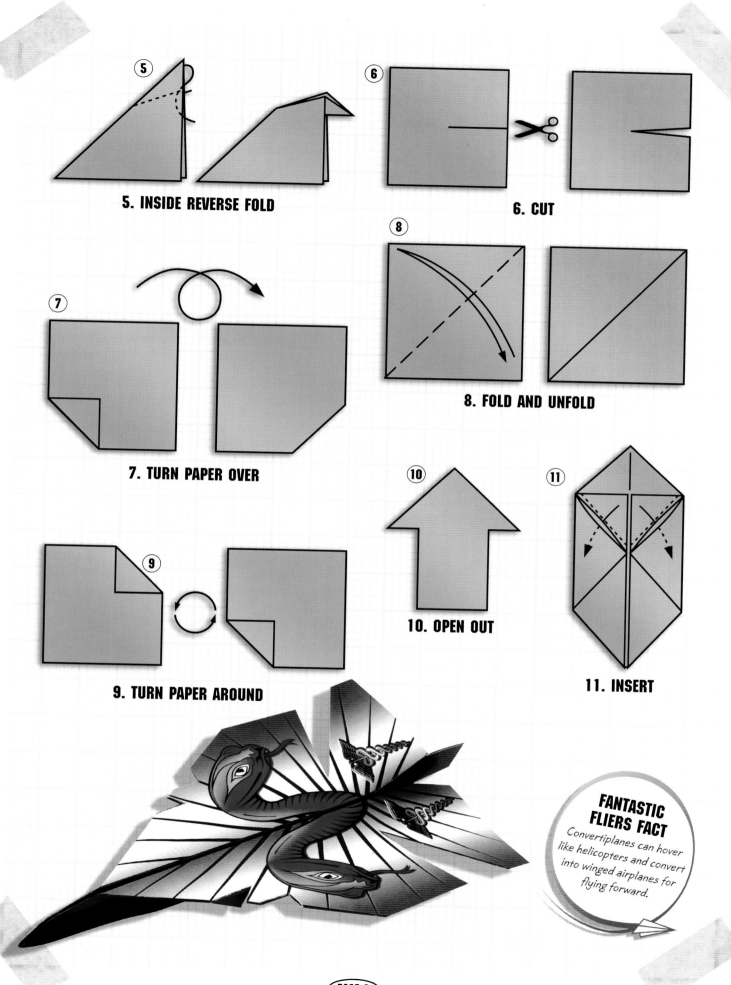

5. INSIDE REVERSE FOLD

6. CUT

7. TURN PAPER OVER

8. FOLD AND UNFOLD

9. TURN PAPER AROUND

10. OPEN OUT

11. INSERT

FANTASTIC FLIERS FACT

Convertiplanes can hover like helicopters and convert into winged airplanes for flying forward.

GROOVY JET

FOLLOW THESE FEW SIMPLE STEPS TO MAKE THE COOLEST JET AROUND.
USE THE PRINTED PAGE NUMBERED 1 AT THE BACK OF THIS SECTION.

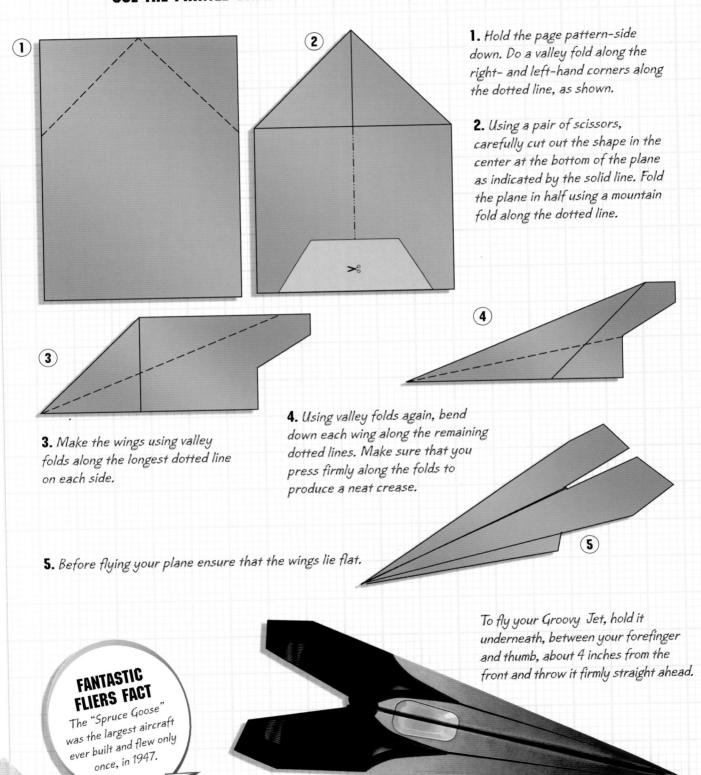

1. Hold the page pattern-side down. Do a valley fold along the right- and left-hand corners along the dotted line, as shown.

2. Using a pair of scissors, carefully cut out the shape in the center at the bottom of the plane as indicated by the solid line. Fold the plane in half using a mountain fold along the dotted line.

3. Make the wings using valley folds along the longest dotted line on each side.

4. Using valley folds again, bend down each wing along the remaining dotted lines. Make sure that you press firmly along the folds to produce a neat crease.

5. Before flying your plane ensure that the wings lie flat.

To fly your Groovy Jet, hold it underneath, between your forefinger and thumb, about 4 inches from the front and throw it firmly straight ahead.

FANTASTIC FLIERS FACT
The "Spruce Goose" was the largest aircraft ever built and flew only once, in 1947.

WHIZZING WEDGE

THIS PLANE WILL WHIZZ THROUGH THE AIR WITH THE GREATEST OF SPEED.
USE THE PRINTED PAGE NUMBERED 2 AT THE BACK OF THIS SECTION.

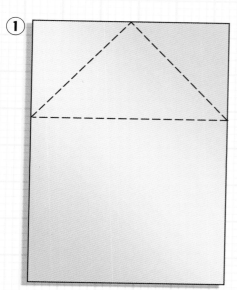

1. Hold the page pattern-side down. Do a valley fold along the right and left hand corners along the dotted line, as shown. Then take the triangle-shaped piece and bend it down in a valley fold, as shown.

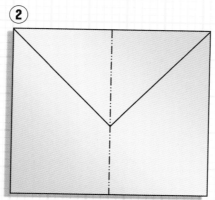

2. Using a mountain fold, fold the whole plane in half.

3. Bend down both sides using the two shortest dotted lines you can see, using valley folds.

4. The wings are made by, again, making valley folds along the remaining visible dotted lines. Make sure that you press firmly to get neatly creased edges.

5. Before making a test flight, make sure the tops of both wings are flat.

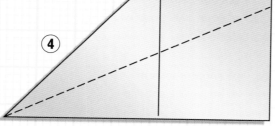

To fly your Whizzing Wedge hold it underneath, between your forefinger and thumb, about 3 inches from the front and throw it firmly straight ahead.

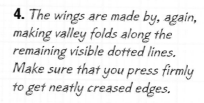

FANTASTIC FLIERS FACT
Chuck Yeager broke the sound barrier in the Bell X-1 in 1947.

GRACEFUL GLIDER

FOLLOW THESE EASY STEPS TO CREATE A GLIDER THAT WILL GENTLY GLIDE ALONG BEFORE COMING TO LAND. USE THE PRINTED PAGE NUMBERED 3 AT THE BACK OF THIS SECTION.

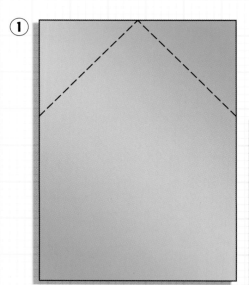

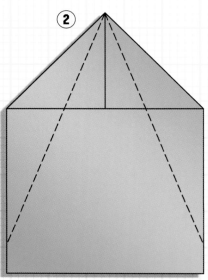

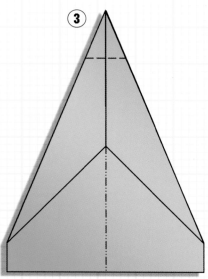

1. Hold the page pattern-side down. Do a valley fold along the right- and left-hand corners along the dotted lines, as shown.

2. Bring in the two sides by bending the dotted edges toward the center in valley folds, as shown.

4. Make the wings by forming valley folds on either side using the long dotted lines as your crease guide. Again, keep all your folds crisp and sharp by pressing firmly.

5. Bend up the corners of both wings using valley folds along the dotted lines.

6. Before flying your plane make sure the wings are angled slightly upward, as shown.

3. Take the pointed tip and pull it down toward you in a valley fold using the dotted line (at the level of the orange segments) for the crease. Fold the whole plane in half by bending a mountain fold along the center line. Keep your creases sharp.

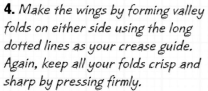

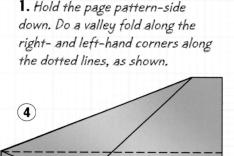

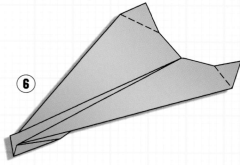

To fly your Graceful Glider, hold it between your forefinger and thumb, about 2 inches from the front. Your glider will perform a graceful glide before diving to the ground.

FANTASTIC FLIERS FACT
Ultralight planes grew out of the sport of hang gliding when people put small engines on hang gliders.

FUNKY FLYER

THIS WIDE-WINGED WONDER WILL ASTOUND YOU WITH ITS SPEED.
USE THE PRINTED PAGE NUMBERED 4 AT THE BACK OF THIS SECTION.

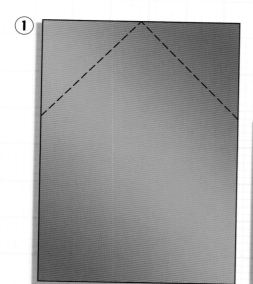

1. Hold the page pattern-side down. Do a valley fold along the right and left-hand corners along the dotted line, as shown.

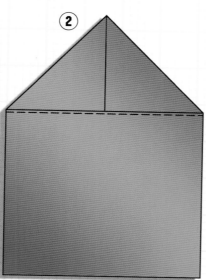

2. Take the triangle-shaped piece and bend it down in a valley fold, as shown. Remember to use the dotted lines as the guide to where to fold.

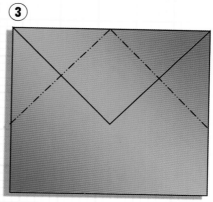

3. Fold the top corners back in a mountain fold, along the dashed line, as shown.

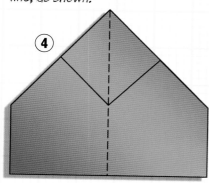

4. Fold the whole plane in half using a valley fold down the center dotted line. Press down firmly to make a neat crease.

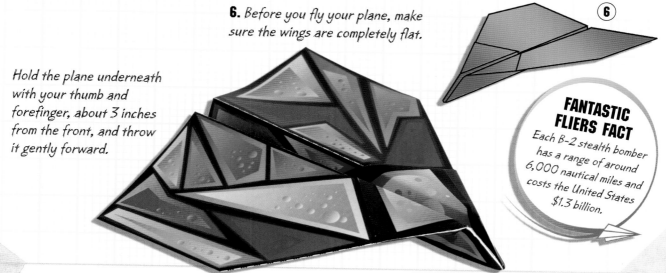

5. To form the wings use valley folds on both sides of the plane. Use the dotted lines to guide your crease line.

6. Before you fly your plane, make sure the wings are completely flat.

Hold the plane underneath with your thumb and forefinger, about 3 inches from the front, and throw it gently forward.

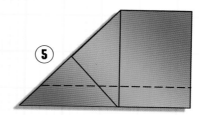

FANTASTIC FLIERS FACT
Each B-2 stealth bomber has a range of around 6,000 nautical miles and costs the United States $1.3 billion.

HIGH FLYER

THIS COOLEST OF FLYERS IS VERY EASY TO DO.
USE THE PRINTED PAGE NUMBERED 5 AT THE BACK OF THIS SECTION.

①

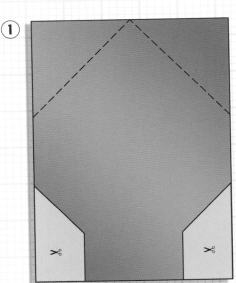

②

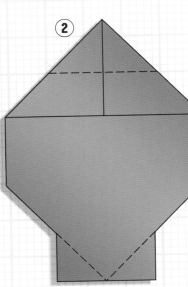

③

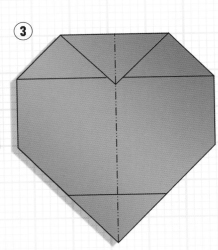

1. Hold the page pattern-side down. Do a valley fold along the top right- and left-hand corners along the dotted line as shown. Using the solid lines as a guide, carefully use a pair of scissors to cut the bottom corners in the shape shown.

2. Take the top triangle-shaped flap and bend it down in a valley fold along the dotted line. Use valley folds to bend up the bottom corners into a V shape.

4. To form the nose, bend valley folds on either side of the plane using the dotted lines as your guide.

3. Fold the plane in half by doing a mountain fold along the central dashed line.

⑤

④

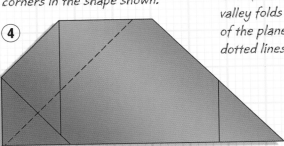

5. Form each wing by making valley folds on either side of the plane.

6. Before you fly your plane, bend the wings slightly upward.

To get your creation airborne, hold it between your forefinger and thumb about 2 inches from the front. Throw it fast and high.

FANTASTIC FLIERS FACT
The Gulfstream V is considered to be the world's first ultra-long-range business jet.

DAREDEVIL DART

THIS DARING DART FLIES HIGH AND FAST.
USE THE PRINTED PAGE NUMBERED 6 AT THE BACK OF THIS SECTION.

①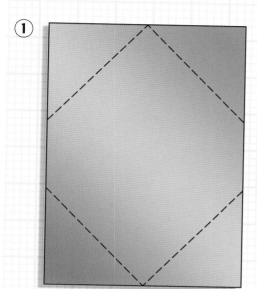

1. Use valley folds to bend in all four corners, as shown.

②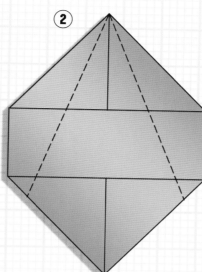

2. Bend in both sides at the top with valley folds, following the long dotted lines as a guide.

③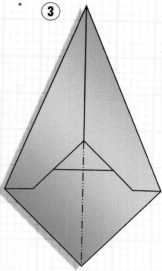

3. Fold the entire plane in half by using a mountain fold along the long dashed center line.

④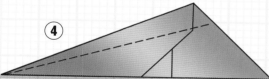

4. The first fold for the wings uses a long valley fold on each side, following the dotted lines.

⑤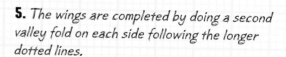

5. The wings are completed by doing a second valley fold on each side following the longer dotted lines.

⑥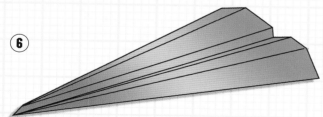

6. Before your flight, bend the outer edges of the wings slightly downward making an M shape.

To fly your Daredevil Dart, hold it underneath between your forefinger and thumb about 5 inches from the front. This plane flies best if thrown gently straight ahead at eye level.

FANTASTIC FLIERS FACT
As the MiG-25 blasts through the air, it gets very hot. Its skin is made from titanium metal which expands and flexes with the heat.

DELTA-WINGED DREAM

THIS DESIGN IS IDEAL FOR BEGINNERS—SIMPLE BUT VERY EFFECTIVE.
USE THE PRINTED PAGE NUMBERED 7 AT THE BACK OF THIS SECTION.

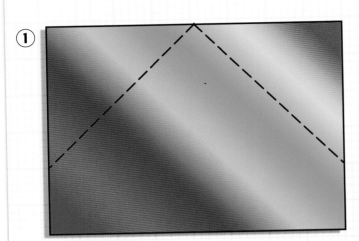

①

②

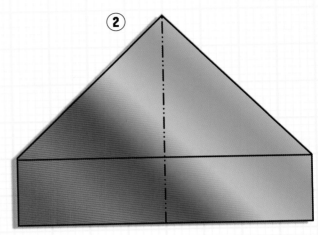

1. Hold the page pattern-side down. Using valley folds, fold the two top corners toward you along the dotted lines.

2. Firmly fold down the center of the plane along the dashed line, using a mountain fold.

③

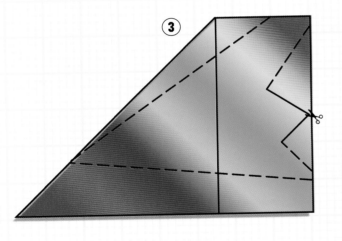

3. Using a pair of scissors, cut along the solid lines, as shown. Now form the shape of the wings and tail by making the remaining valley folds on both sides of the plane's body as indicated by the dotted lines.

Hold the plane in the center of the base and release gently.

FANTASTIC FLIERS FACT
In 1929, the Travel Air Mystery Ship became the first plane raced by a civilian to beat a military flier.

Problems flying your plane? Try weighting down the nose with a paper clip.

LIGHTNING

CUNNING MANEUVERS ARE THIS PLANE'S SPECIALITY—WHY NOT TAKE IT FOR A SPIN? USE THE PRINTED PAGE NUMBERED 8 AT THE BACK OF THIS SECTION.

①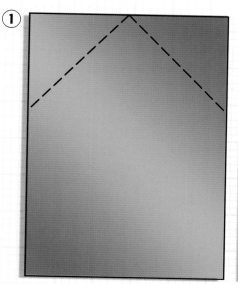

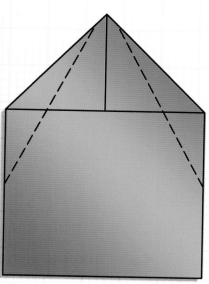

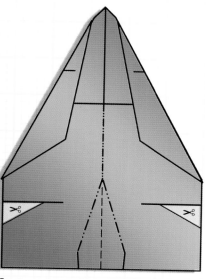

1. Hold the page pattern-side down. Using valley folds, fold the top corners along the dotted lines.

2. Make two more valley folds along the diagonal dotted lines.

3. Cut along all the solid lines around the wing area as shown. Then make a mountain fold along the dashed line running down the center of the plane. Form a short valley fold between the two diagonal mountain folds at the rear.

④

4. Next, cut along the solid lines around the tail area. Form the wings and tail fins by making the remaining valley folds on both sides of the plane's body as indicated by the dotted lines.

Hold the underside of your plane, around 4 inches from the tip, and give it a firm throw.

FANTASTIC FLIERS FACT
Pan Am China Clipper flying boats were introduced in 1935 to fly from San Francisco to China.

BRILLIANT BLACKBIRD

THIS POWERFUL PLANE HAS A DISTINCTIVE DESIGN AND THE GRACE OF A BIRD.
USE THE PRINTED PAGE NUMBERED 9 AT THE BACK OF THIS SECTION.

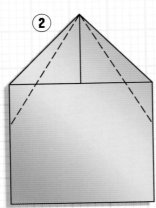 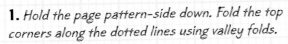 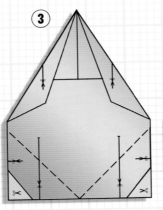 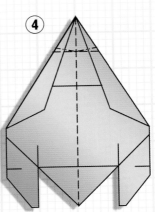

1. *Hold the page pattern-side down. Fold the top corners along the dotted lines using valley folds.*

2. *Make two more valley folds along the diagonal dotted lines.*

3. *Using a pair of scissors, snip off the two bottom corners and then cut along the six solid lines where indicated. Now use diagonal valley folds to shape the rear of the plane, as shown.*

4. *Now fold the triangular tip toward you, using a valley fold, along the straight dotted line. Make two mountain folds along the diagonal dotted lines folding the triangular tip back on itself. Firmly fold the plane down its center along the dotted line ensuring that the folds in the pointed tip stay securely tucked in place.*

5. *Slot the tail fins up through the body of the plane using the two folds shown.*

6. *Finally, make the remaining valley and mountain folds on both sides of the plane's body as indicated by the dotted and dashed lines.*

Holding the bottom of the plane, pinch the wings together, approximately 4 inches from the tip, and gently release.

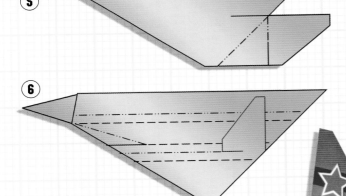

FANTASTIC FLIERS FACT
NASA Super Guppies have a cargo compartment 25 feet tall and wide, and a hinged nose.

SPECTACULAR STRIKEFIGHTER

MAKE THIS STUNNING STRIKEFIGHTER IN MINUTES.
USE THE PRINTED PAGE NUMBERED 10 AT THE BACK OF THIS SECTION.

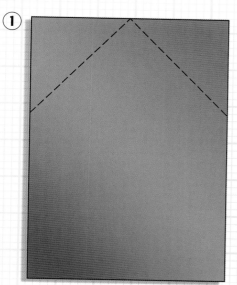

1. Hold the page pattern-side down. Using valley folds, fold in the top two corners.

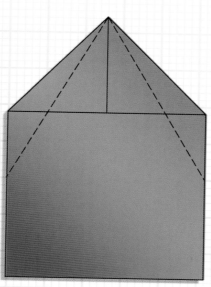

2. Make two more valley folds along the two diagonal dotted lines.

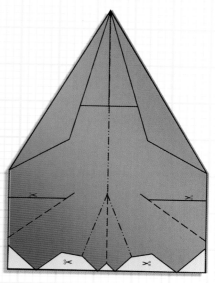

3. Using scissors, cut along the solid lines around the tail and wings. Make a mountain fold along the dashed line running down the center of the plane. Form a short valley fold between the two diagonal mountain folds at the rear of the plane. Now make horizontal cuts on each rear wing and fold the flaps under each slit along the dotted lines, as shown.

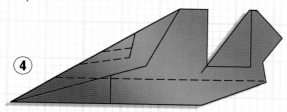

4. Make valley folds along the dotted lines on the wings as shown. Using more valley folds, form the front wings on either side of the plane.

Throw the plane gently, holding it approximately 4 inches from the tip.

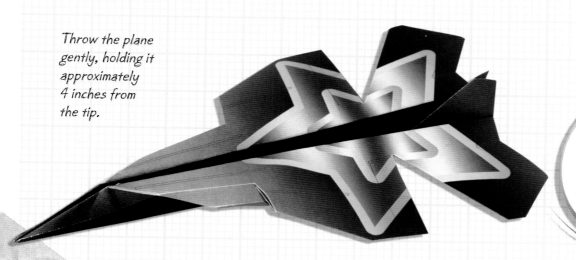

FANTASTIC FLIERS FACT
The "Explorer" amphibious powered parachute is the only aircraft of its kind in the world.

SUPERCOOL SUPERSONIC

TRY THIS CLASSIC DESIGN—IT'LL FLY LIKE A DREAM.
USE THE PRINTED PAGE NUMBERED 11 AT THE BACK OF THIS SECTION.

1. Hold the page pattern-side down. Fold in the top two corners using valley folds.

2. Now fold the triangular tip toward you, using a valley fold, along the straight dotted line. Next, make two mountain folds along the diagonal dashed lines folding the triangular tip back on itself.

3. Firmly fold the plane down its center, using a valley fold, ensuring that the folds in the pointed tip stay securely tucked in place.

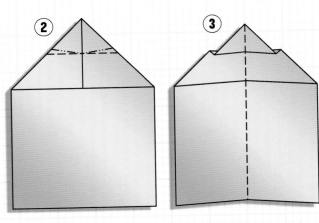

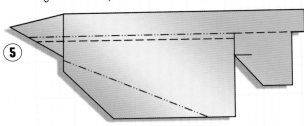

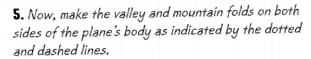

4. Using a pair of scissors, carefully cut out the tail and wing shapes using the solid lines as a guide.

5. Now, make the valley and mountain folds on both sides of the plane's body as indicated by the dotted and dashed lines.

6. Using mountain folds, tuck the tail into position through the slit at the rear of the plane making sure that it interlocks.

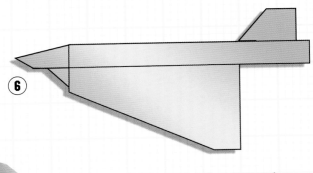

Slot your forefinger into the underside the wings, around 2 inches from the tip, and gently throw your plane.

FANTASTIC FLIERS FACT

The Polaris Flying Inflatable Boat was patented by Polaris Motor SRL and Lomac Nautica in 1986.

TERRIFIC TORNADO

THIS EUROPEAN TORNADO IS SUPER SPEEDY AND YET SIMPLE TO MAKE!
USE THE PRINTED PAGE NUMBERED 12 AT THE BACK OF THIS SECTION.

①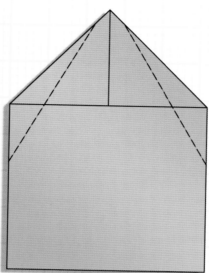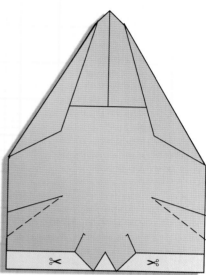

1. Hold the page pattern-side down. Using valley folds, bend in the two top corners.

2. Make two valley folds along the diagonal dotted lines.

3. Using a pair of scissors, carefully cut along the solid lines to begin forming the wings and tail shape. Below the top set of slits, make two diagonal valley folds to create the side tail fins.

④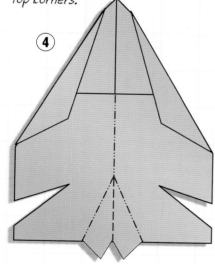

4. Make a mountain fold along the dashed line running down the center of the plane, then two valley folds either side of this line. Fold the wings over. Then form a short valley fold between the two diagonal mountain folds at the rear of the plane.

⑤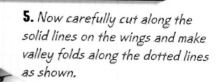

5. Now carefully cut along the solid lines on the wings and make valley folds along the dotted lines as shown.

Throw the plane gently, holding it approximately 5 inches from the tip.

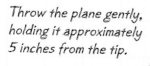

FANTASTIC FLIERS FACT
Brian Milton became the first man to fly around the world in a ultralight, in 1988.

MAGNIFICENT MIRAGE

MAKE THIS MARVELOUS MIRAGE FIGHTER FOR SUPERCOOL MISSIONS. USE THE PRINTED PAGE NUMBERED 13 AT THE BACK OF THIS SECTION.

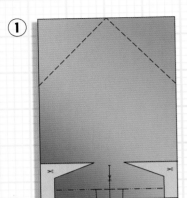
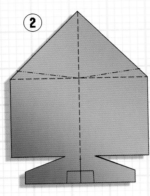
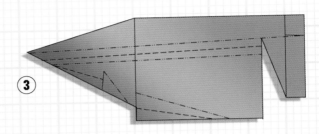

1. Fold in the two top corners along the dotted lines using valley folds. Cut three slits at the bottom along the solid lines. Cut away the surplus tail section. Fold the outer flaps under using mountain folds and the inner flaps out using valley folds.

2. Now fold the pointed tip toward you using a valley fold along the straight line. Next, make two mountain folds along the diagonal lines by folding the pointed tip back on itself. Firmly fold the plane down its center, using a valley fold, ensuring that the folds in the pointed tip stay securely tucked in place.

3. Cut a slit toward the front of the wings as indicated by another solid line. Then using a series of valley folds and mountain folds along the edges, form the basic shape of the plane.

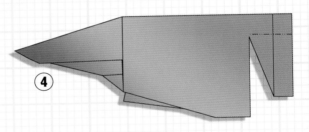

4. Fold up the wing tips using a valley fold and a mountain fold on each wing. Secure the tail by tucking the flap from one side around the other and interlock them.

To fly your plane, hold it about 3 inches from the front and throw it gently forward.

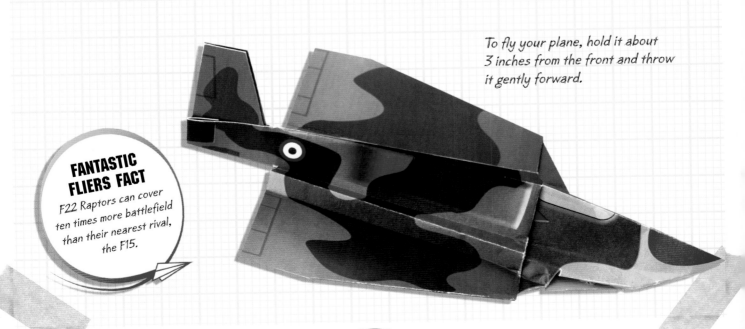

FANTASTIC FLIERS FACT
F22 Raptors can cover ten times more battlefield than their nearest rival, the F15.

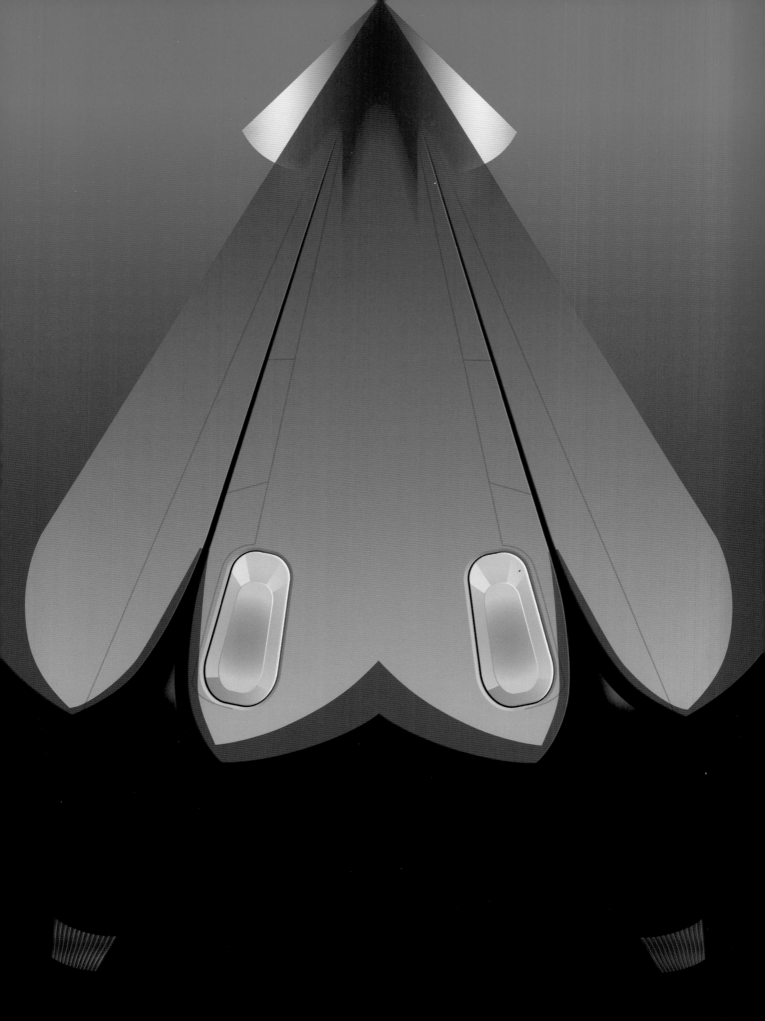

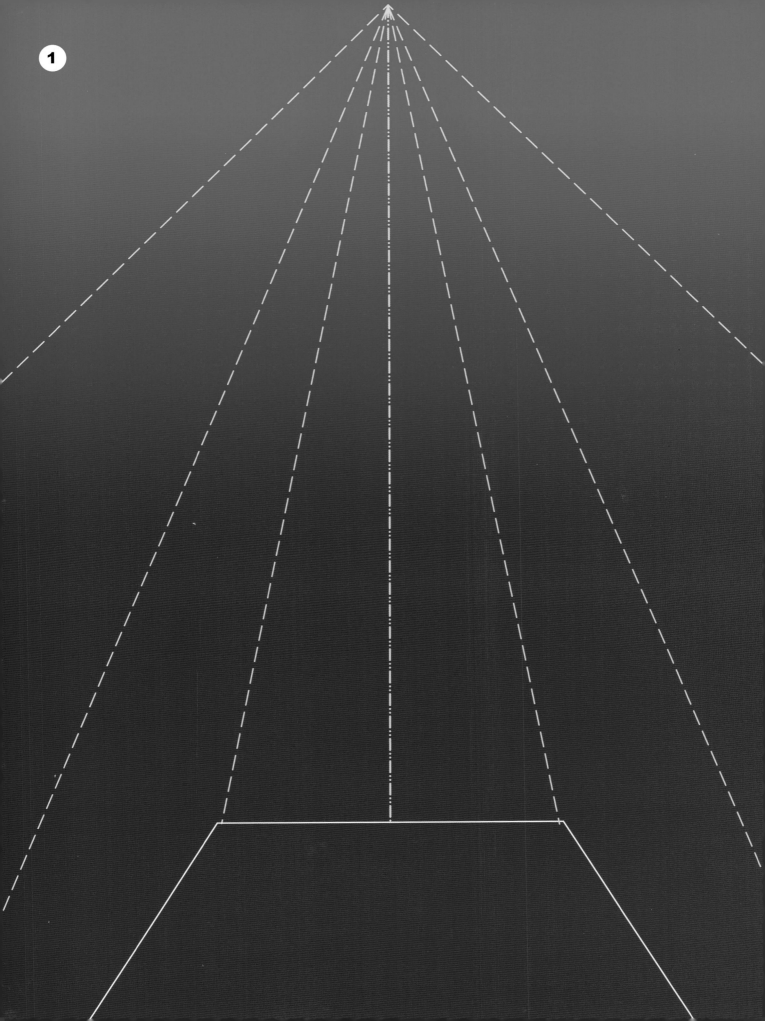

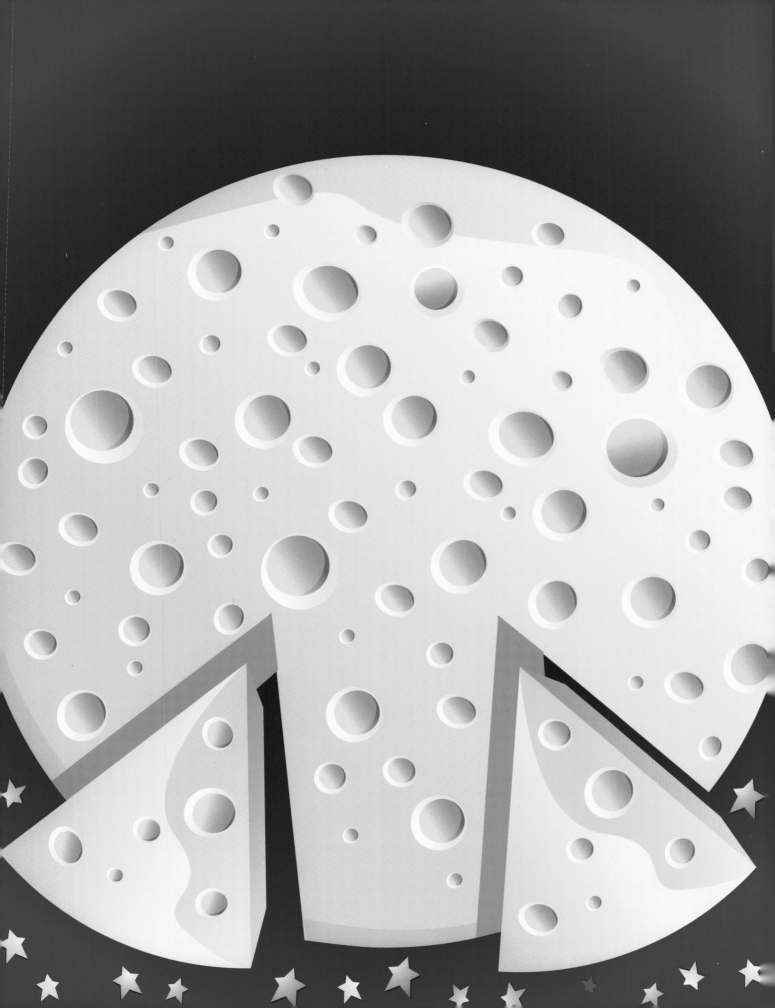

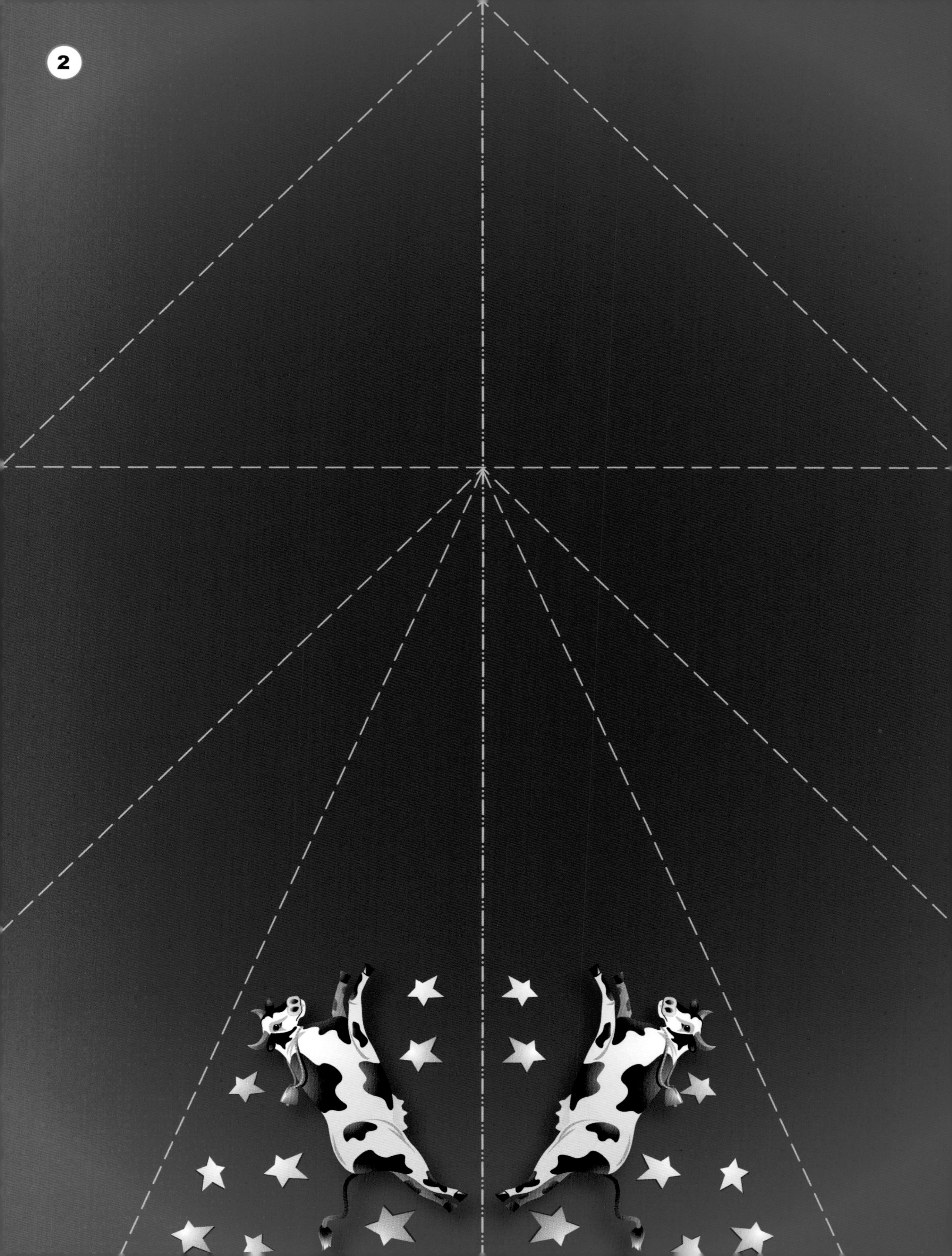
2

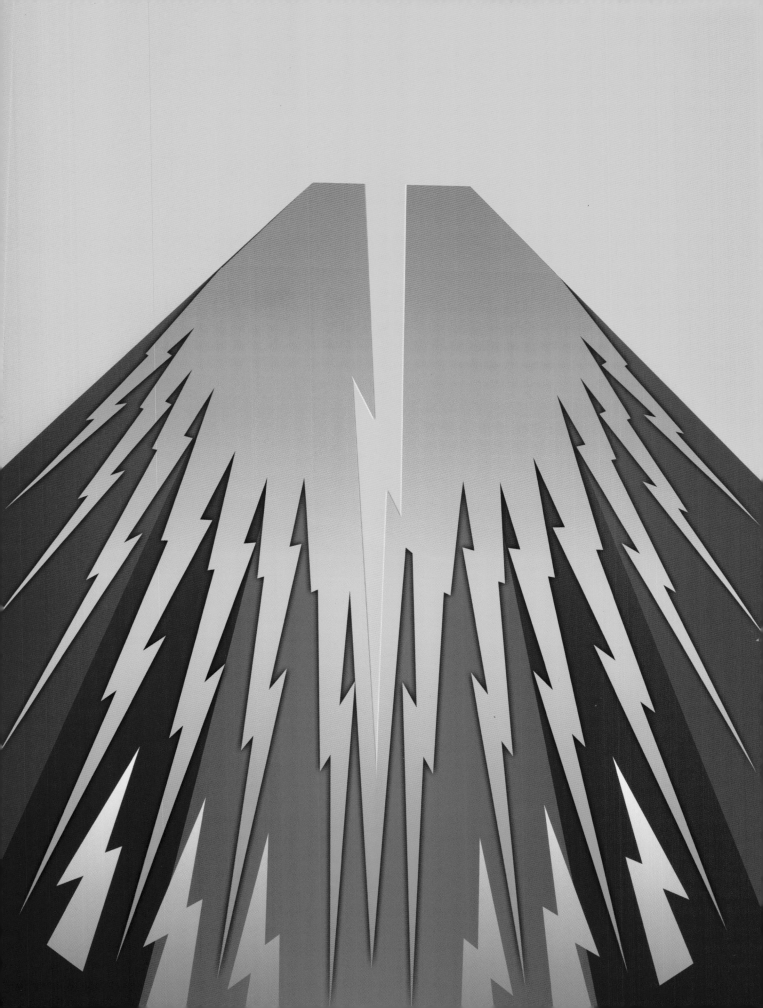

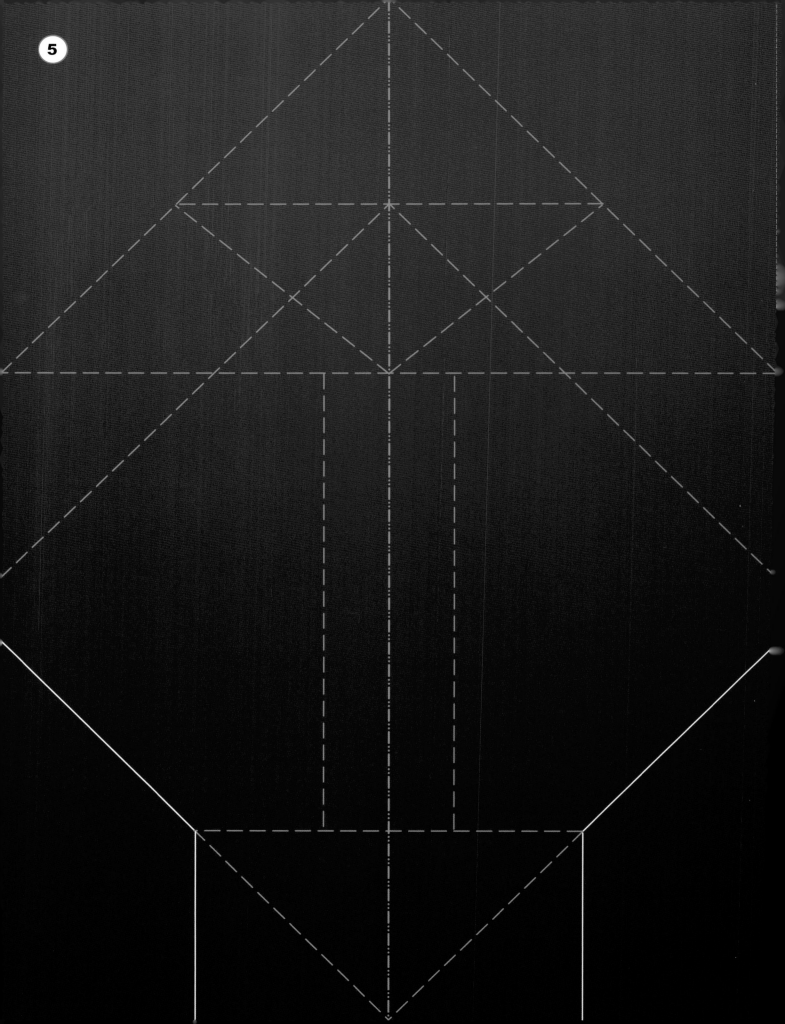

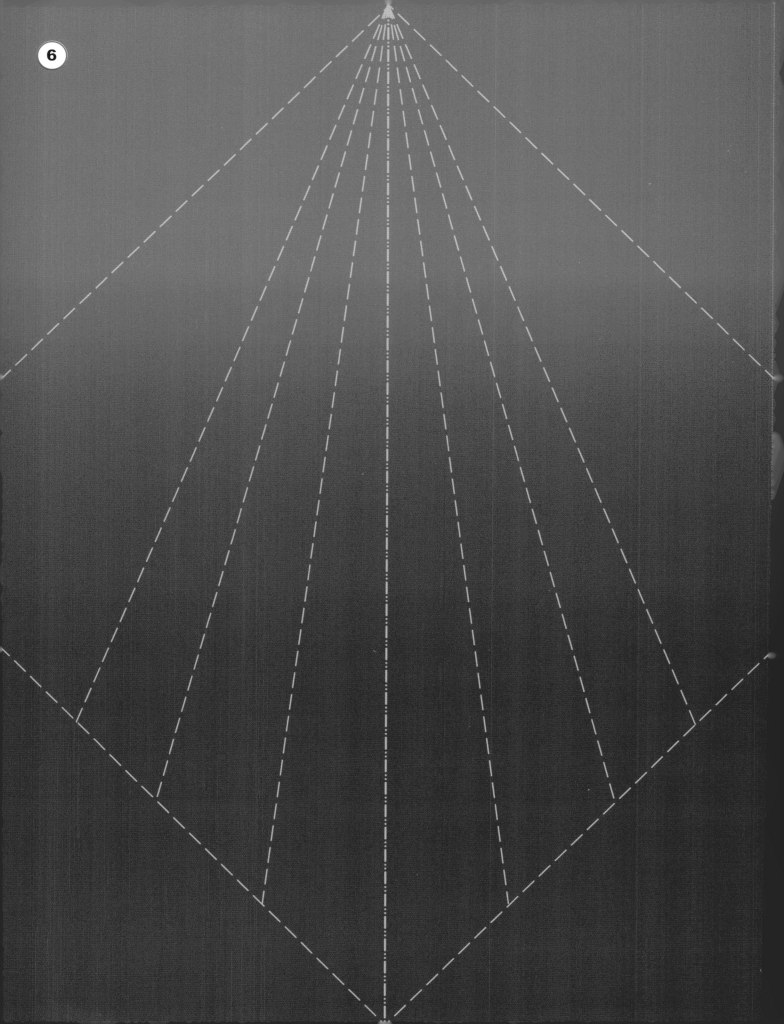

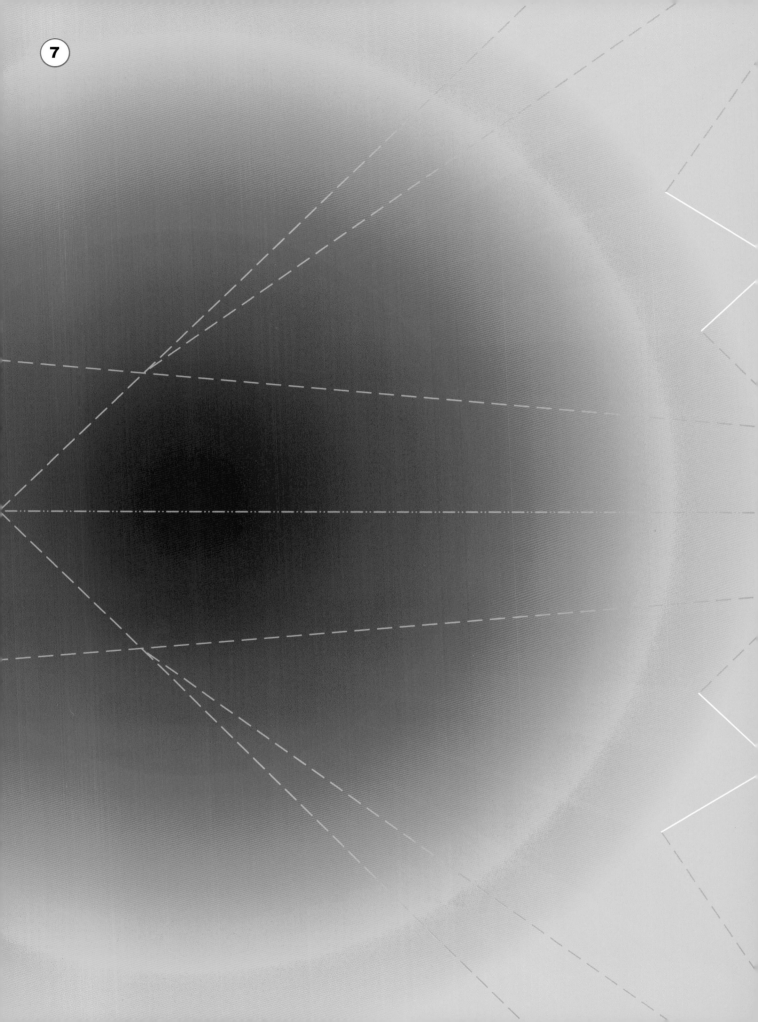

8

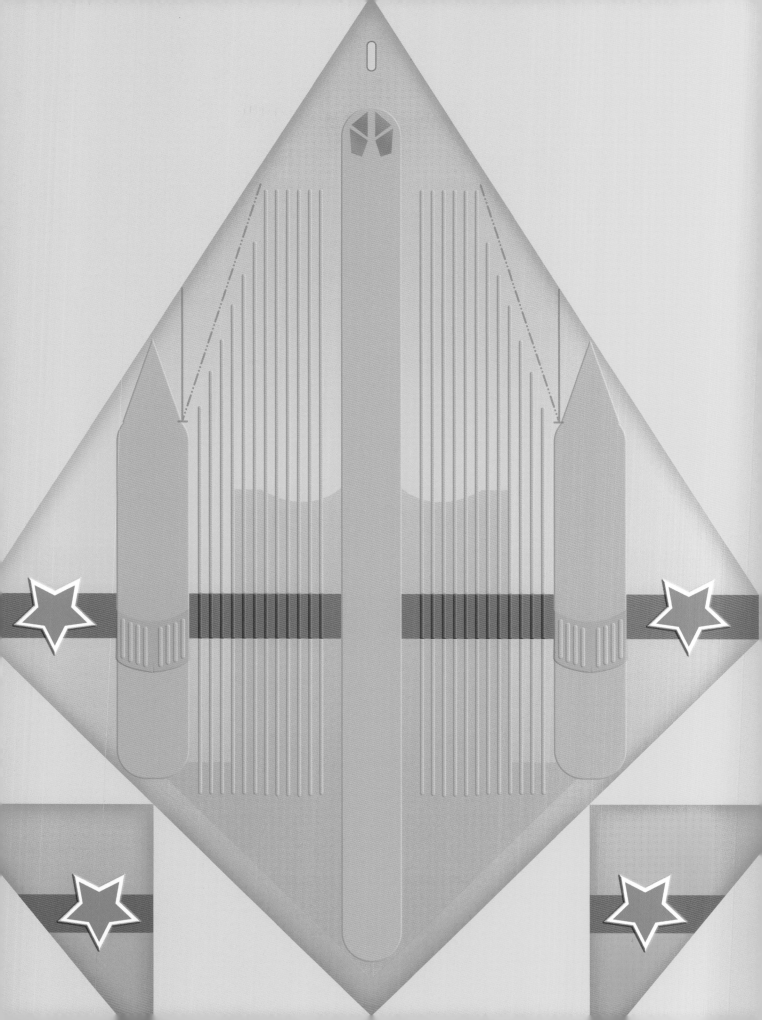

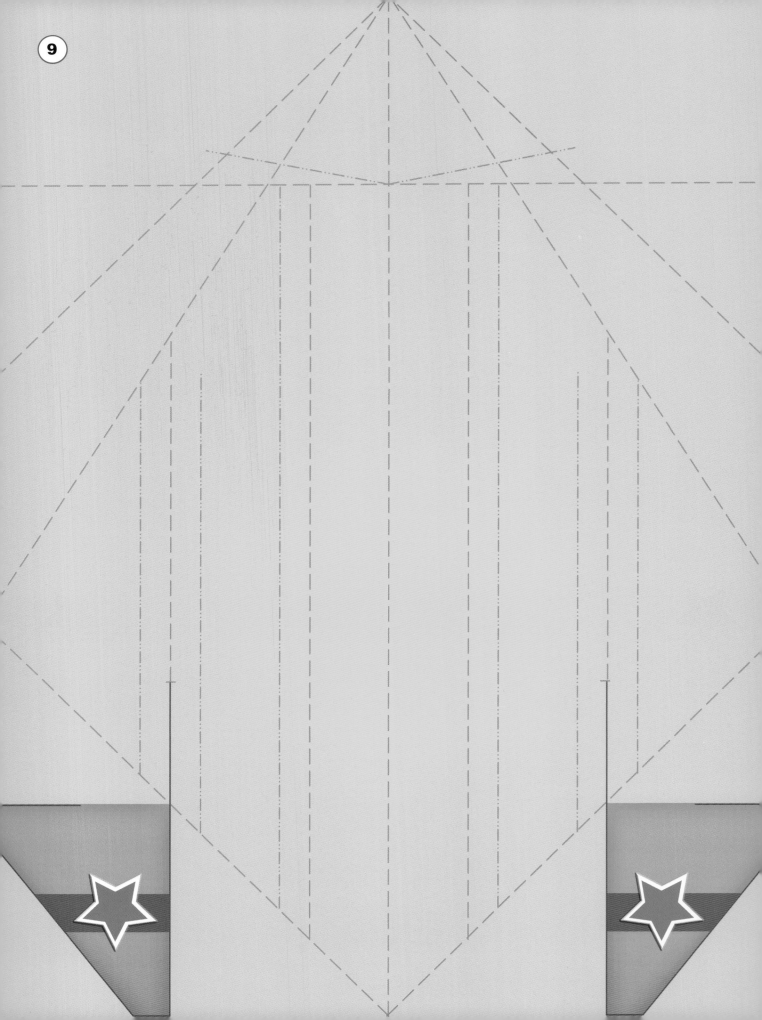

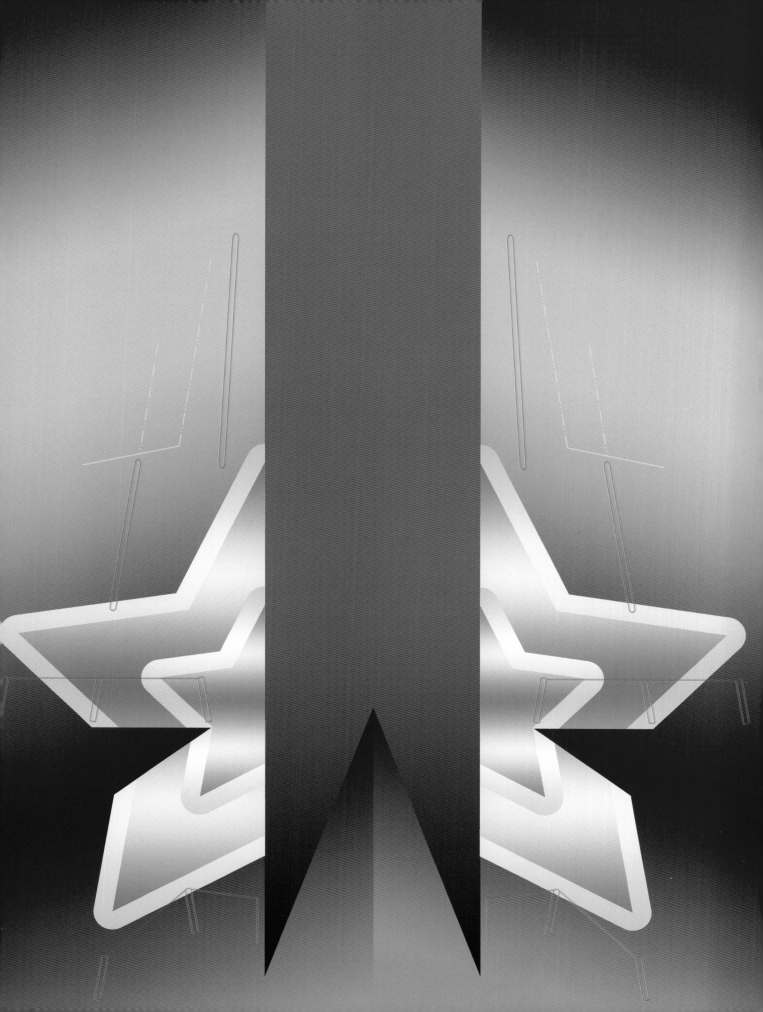

11

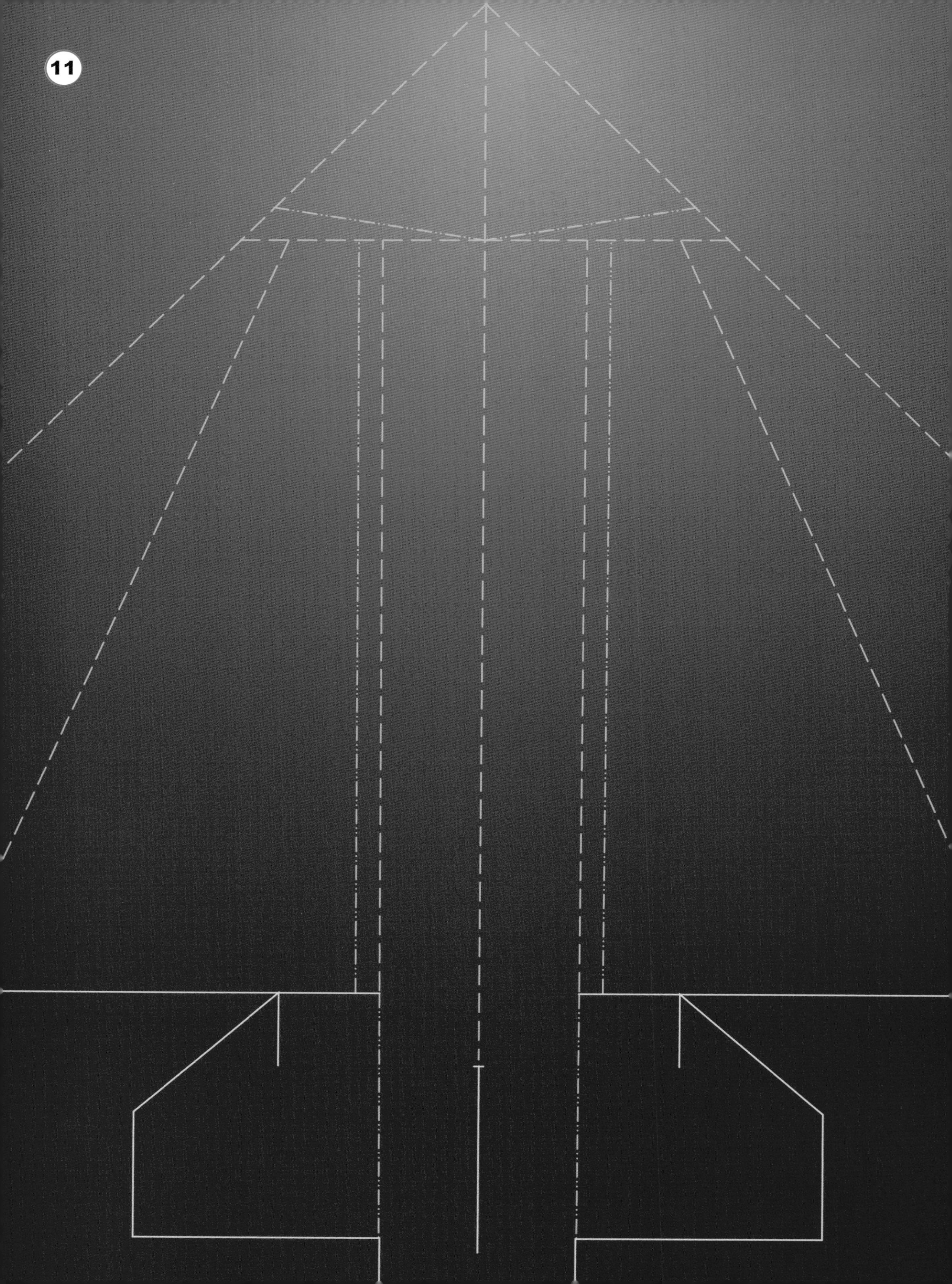

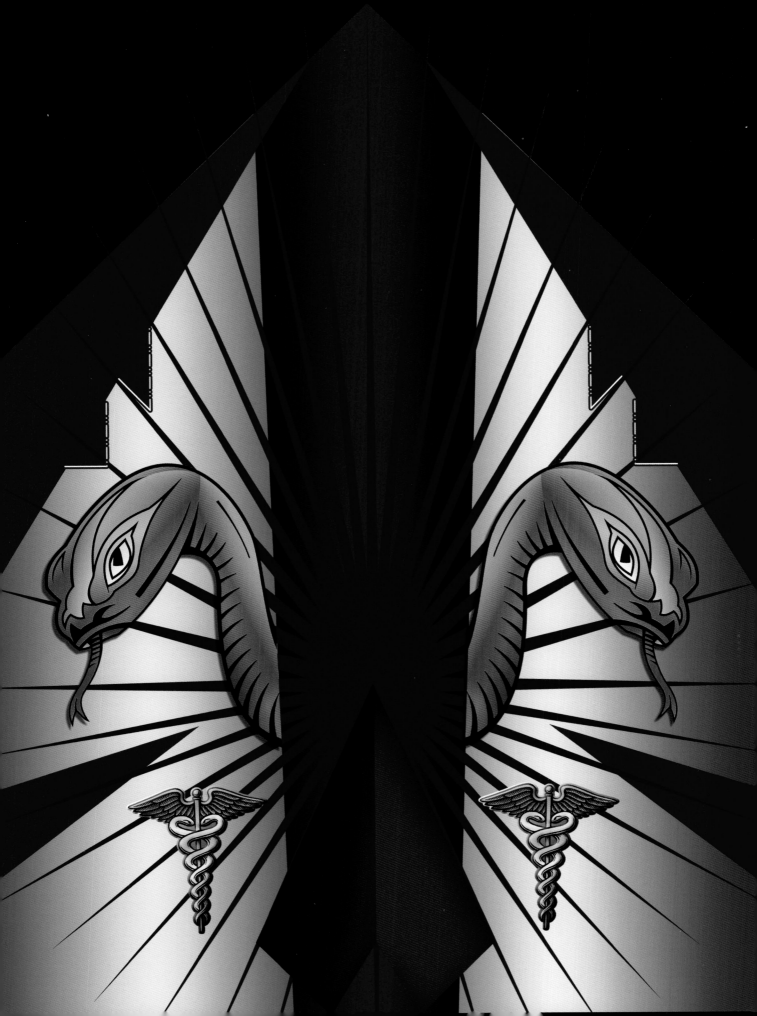

13

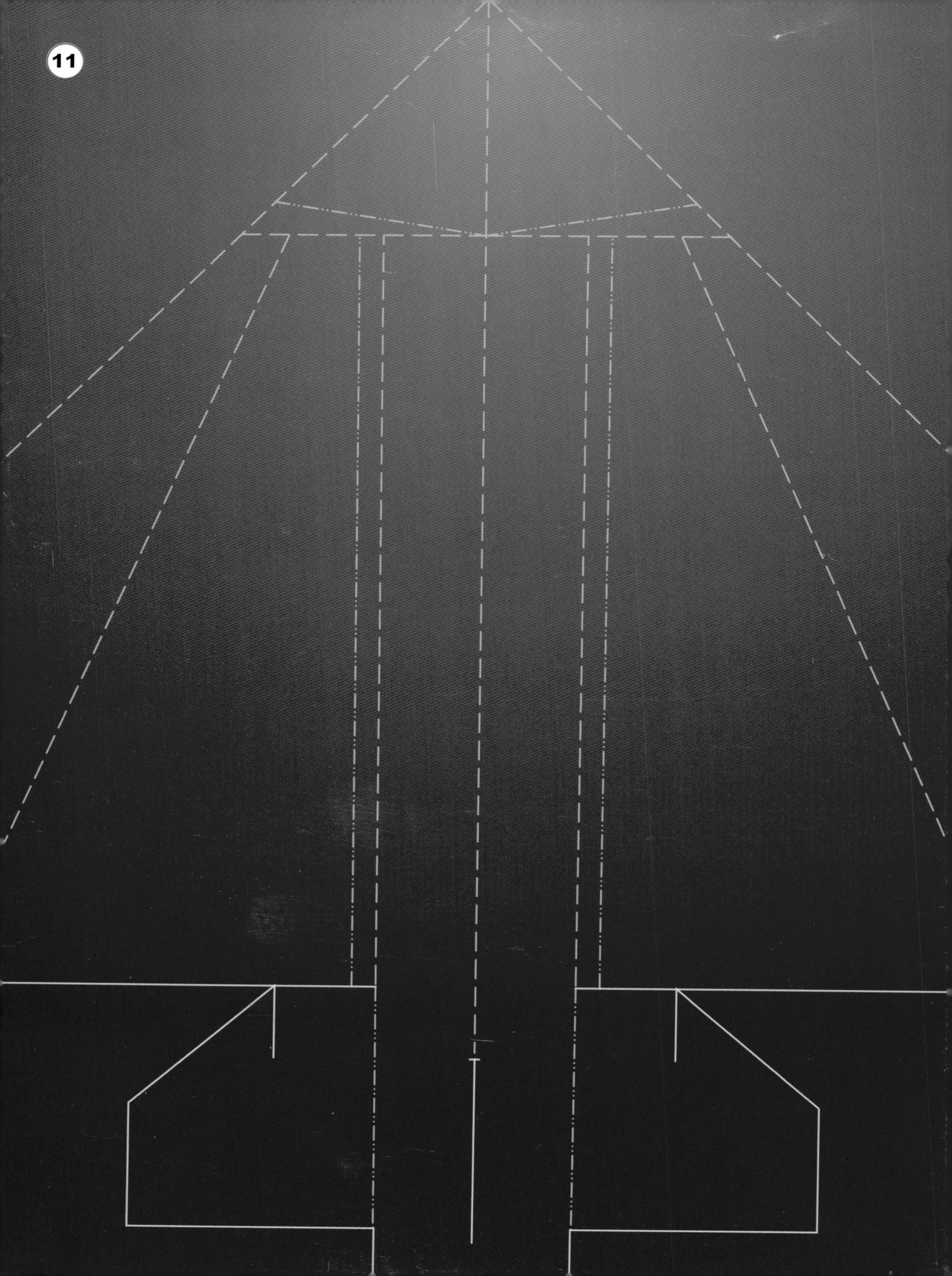
11

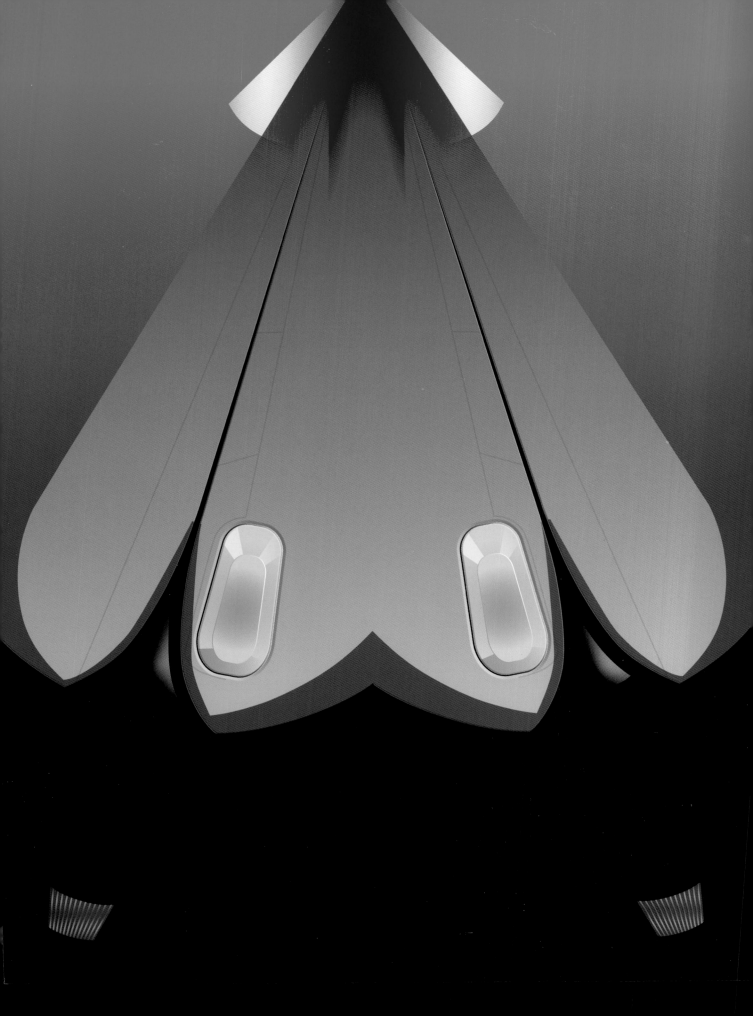

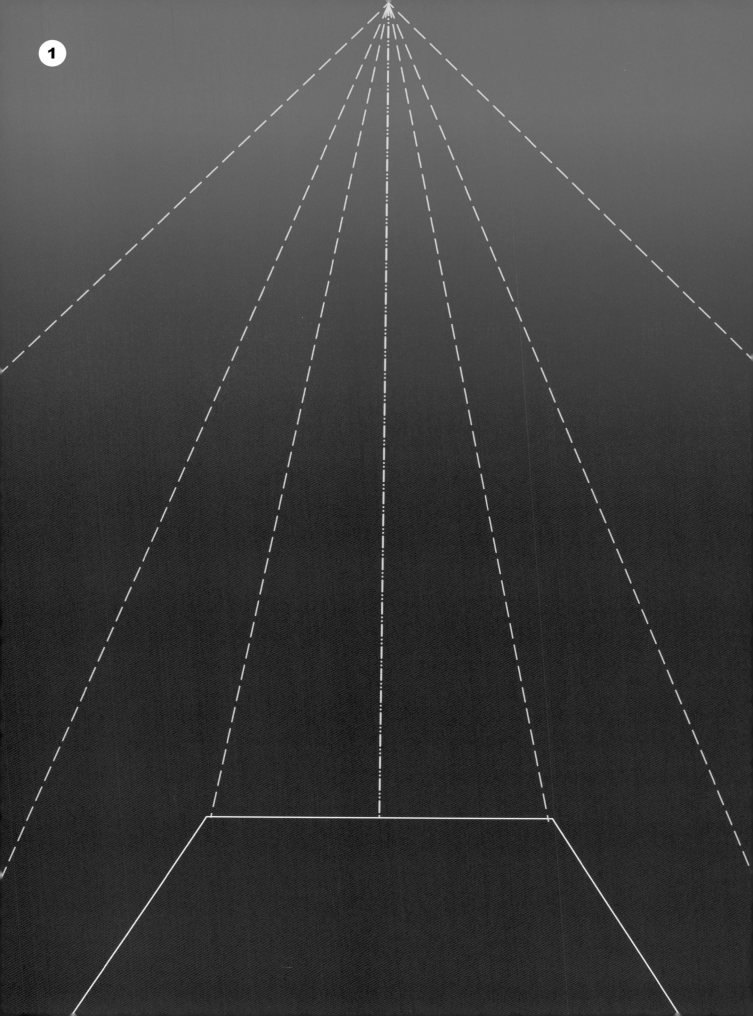